HMH

math
expressions

Dr. Karen C. Fuson

Watch the frog come alive in its pond as you discover
and solve math challenges.

Download the *Math Worlds AR* app available on Android or iOS devices.

Grade 1

Volume 1

This material is based upon work supported by the
National Science Foundation
under Grant Numbers
ESI-9816320, REC-9806020, and RED-935373.

Any opinions, findings, and conclusions, or recommendations expressed in this material
are those of the author and do not necessarily reflect the views of the National Science Foundation.

Printed in the U.S.A.

ISBN 978-1-328-74381-7

5 6 7 8 9 10   0868   26 25 24 23 22 21 20 19

4500757946   C D E F G

BIG IDEA 3 - Find and Create Patterns

BIG IDEA 1 - Represent Addition Situations

BIG IDEA 2 - Solve Addition Equations

BIG IDEA 3 - Mixed Story Problems

© Houghton Mifflin Harcourt Publishing Company

Dear Family:

Your child is learning math in an innovative program that interweaves abstract mathematical concepts with the everyday experiences of children. This helps children to understand math better.

In this program, your child will learn math and have fun by

- working with objects and making drawings of math situations
- working with other children and sharing problem-solving strategies with them
- writing and solving problems and connecting math to daily life
- helping classmates learn

Your child will have homework almost every day. He or she needs a **Homework Helper.** The helper may be anyone—you, an older brother or sister (or other family member), a neighbor, or a friend. Make a specific time for homework and provide your child with a quiet place to work (for example, no TV). Encourage your child to talk about what is happening in math class.

In Lessons 1 and 2, your child will learn to see numbers as a group of 5 and extra ones. Making mental pictures by grouping units in this way will later help your child add and subtract quickly. Children benefit greatly from learning to "see" numbers without counting every unit.

- -

Please fill out the following and return it to the teacher.

My child _____ will have _____ as his or her
           (child's name)   (Homework Helper's name)

Homework Helper. This person is my child's _____.
                                     (relationship to child)

Children start exploring these 5-groups by looking at dots arranged in a row of 5 plus some extra ones. Below are samples that show the numbers from 6 through 10.

5 + 1   5 + 2   5 + 3   5 + 4   5 + 5

The teacher gives the children a number and asks them to say it as a 5 plus extra ones. Children say the numbers in order at first. Later they can "see" the quantities even when the numbers are shown randomly.

On some homework pages, you will find instructions that ask children to "see the 5." Your child is being encouraged to make a mental picture of a number that contains a 5-group. Later, the children will be asked to see groups of 10 by combining two 5-groups. This will help them learn place value.

It takes repeated exposure to such groups for children to see the numbers quickly. Many of the visual aids in your child's classroom include 5-groups. Children tend to absorb these visual patterns without realizing it.

If you have any questions or if your child is having problems with math, please contact me.

Sincerely,
Your child's teacher

Estimada familia:

Su niño está aprendiendo matemáticas con un programa innovador que relaciona conceptos matemáticos abstractos con la experiencia diaria de los niños. Esto ayuda a los niños a entender mejor las matemáticas.

Con este programa, su niño aprenderá matemáticas y se divertirá mientras:

- trabaja con objetos y hace dibujos de problemas matemáticos;
- trabaja con otros niños y comparte estrategias para resolver problemas;
- escribe y resuelve problemas y relaciona las matemáticas con la vida diaria;
- ayuda a sus compañeros a aprender.

Su niño tendrá tarea casi todos los días y necesita a una persona que lo ayude con la tarea. Esa persona puede ser usted, un hermano mayor (u otro familiar), un vecino o un amigo. Establezca una hora para la tarea y ofrezca a su niño un lugar tranquilo donde trabajar (por ejemplo un lugar sin TV). Anime a su niño a comentar lo que está aprendiendo en la clase de matemáticas.

En las Lecciones 1 y 2, su niño aprenderá a ver los números como un grupo de 5 más otras unidades. El hecho de agrupar mentalmente unidades de esa manera ayudará a su niño a sumar y restar rápidamente en el futuro. Los niños se benefician muchísimo de aprender a "ver" los números sin contar cada unidad.

- -

Por favor complete la siguiente información y devuelva este formulario al maestro.

La persona que ayudará a mi niño _____ es
                                                (nombre del niño)

_____ . Esta persona es _____ de mi niño.
   (nombre de la persona)   (relación con el niño)

Los niños comienzan a practicar con estos grupos de 5 observando puntos distribuidos en una fila de 5 más otras unidades. Estos ejemplos muestran los números del 6 al 10.

5 + 1   5 + 2   5 + 3   5 + 4   5 + 5

El maestro les da un número a los niños y les pide que lo digan como 5 más otras unidades. Al principio, los niños dicen los números en orden. Más adelante pueden "ver" las cantidades incluso cuando los números se muestran sin un orden específico.

En algunas páginas de tarea hallará instrucciones que piden a los niños "ver el número 5". A su niño se le está animando a que visualice un número que contenga un grupo de 5. Más adelante, se les pedirá que vean grupos de 10, combinando dos grupos de 5. Esto les ayudará a aprender el valor posicional.

Es necesario que los niños practiquen muchas veces los grupos de este tipo para que puedan llegar a ver los números rápidamente. Muchas de las ayudas visuales que hay en el salón de clase incluyen grupos de 5. Los niños tienden a absorber estos patrones visuales sin darse cuenta.

Si tiene alguna pregunta o algún comentario, por favor comuníquese conmigo.

Atentamente,
El maestro de su niño

doubles

repeating pattern

growing pattern

shrinking pattern

pattern

▲■▲■▲■▲■▲■▲■

$4 + 4 = 8$

Both partners are the same.
They are **doubles**.

4 3 2 1

1 2 3 4

The partners of a number
show a **pattern**.

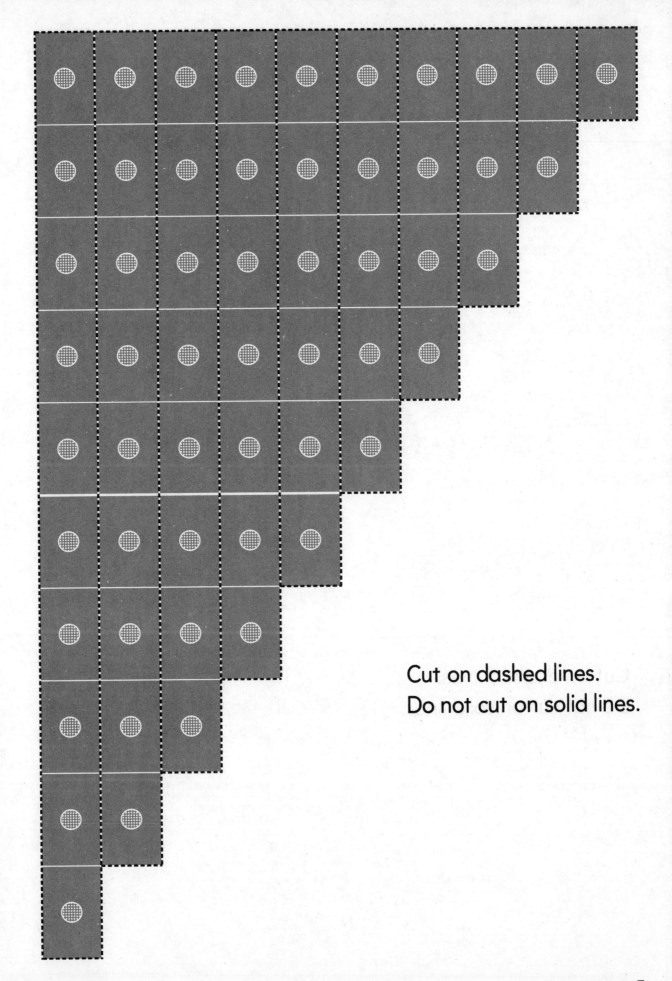

Cut on dashed lines.
Do not cut on solid lines.

Stair Steps **5**

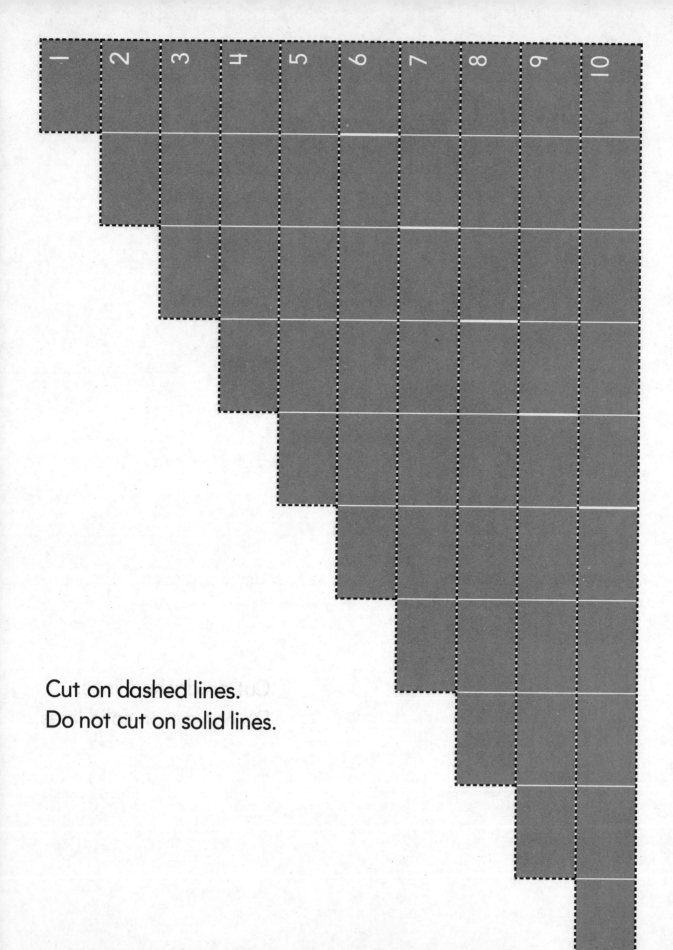

Cut on dashed lines.
Do not cut on solid lines.

Stair Steps

6	1
7	2
8	3
9	4
10	5

Name _____

Circle the 5-group. Write how many dots.

1

☐

2

☐

3

☐

4

☐

5

☐

6

☐

7 Match the dots to 5 plus extra ones.

 • • **5 + 1**

 • • **5 + 3**

 • • **5 + 4**

• • **5 + 2**

• • **5 + 5**

8 Draw a 5-group and extra ones to show 6.

9 Draw a 5-group and extra ones to show 9.

10 Create a story for 7. Draw a 5-group and extra ones to show your story.

_____

_____

_____

_____

✓ **Check Understanding**
Show numbers 6 through 10 as 5-groups and extra ones.

Visualize Numbers as a 5-Group and Ones

Name _____   Date _____

See the 5-group.
Draw extra dots to show the number.

1 8

2 10

See the 5 in each group.
Write how many dots.

3

4

5

Name _____

Date _____

1 Show 9 with a 5-group and extra ones.

2 Use words or pictures to tell a story for 9.

Dear Family:

Your child is learning to find the smaller numbers that are "hiding" inside a larger number. He or she will be participating in activities that will help him or her master addition, subtraction, and equation building.

To make the concepts clear, this program uses some special vocabulary and materials that we would like to share. Below are two important terms that your child is learning:

- **Partners:** Partners are two numbers that can be put together to make a larger number. For example, 2 and 5 are partners that go together to make the number 7.

- **Break Apart:** Children can "break apart" a larger number to form two smaller numbers. Your child is using objects and drawings to explore ways of "breaking apart" numbers of ten or less.

Partners of 7

Children can discover the break-aparts of a number with circle drawings. They first draw the "Break-Apart Stick" and then color the circles to show the different partners, as shown below. Sometimes they also write the partners on a special partner train, which is also shown below.

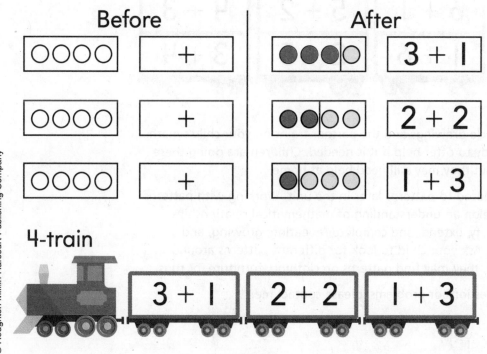

Later, children will discover that partners can change places without changing the total. This concept is called "switch the partners." Once children understand switching partners, they can find the break-aparts of a number more quickly. They simply switch each pair of partners as they discover them.

Shown below are the break-aparts and switched partners of the number 7. Sometimes children also write this information on a double-decker train.

Break-Aparts of 7

$6 + 1$	or	$1 + 6$

$5 + 2$	or	$2 + 5$

$4 + 3$	or	$3 + 4$

Double-Decker Train

7-train

$6 + 1$	$5 + 2$	$4 + 3$
$1 + 6$	$2 + 5$	$3 + 4$

You will see the circle drawings and the partner trains on your child's math homework. Be ready to offer help if it is needed. Children are doing these activities in class, but they may still need help at home.

Children are introduced to patterns later in the unit. Working with patterns helps children develop an understanding of mathematical relationships. They learn to identify, extend, and complete repeating, growing, and shrinking patterns. Ask your child to look for different patterns around them. For example, they may find patterns on clothing, furniture, or rugs.

If you have any questions or problems, please contact me.

Sincerely,
Your child's teacher

Estimada familia:

Su niño está aprendiendo a hallar los números más pequeños que están "escondidos" dentro de un número más grande. Va a participar en actividades que le ayudarán a dominar la suma, la resta y la formación de ecuaciones.

Para clarificar los conceptos, este programa usa un vocabulario especial y algunos materiales que nos gustaría mostrarle. A continuación hay dos términos importantes que su niño está aprendiendo:

- **Partes:** Partes son dos números que se pueden unir para formar un número más grande. Por ejemplo, 2 y 5 son partes que se unen para formar el número 7.

- **Separar:** Los niños pueden "separar" un número más grande para formar dos números más pequeños. Su niño está usando objetos y dibujos para explorar maneras de "separar" números iguales o menores que diez.

Partes de 7

Los niños pueden separar un número usando dibujos de círculos. Primero dibujan un "palito de separación" y luego colorean los círculos para indicar las partes, como se muestra a continuación. A veces los niños anotan las partes en un tren de partes especial, que también se muestra a continuación.

Luego, los niños van a aprender que las partes pueden intercambiar su posición sin que varíe el total. Este concepto se llama "cambiar el orden de las partes". Una vez que los niños entienden el cambio del orden de las partes, pueden encontrar las partes de un número con más rapidez. Sencillamente cambian cada par de partes a medida que las encuentran.

A continuación están las partes, y las partes en otro orden, del número 7. A veces los niños escriben esta información en un tren de dos pisos.

Partes de 7

| $6 + 1$ | y | $1 + 6$ |

| $5 + 2$ | y | $2 + 5$ |

| $4 + 3$ | y | $3 + 4$ |

Tren de dos pisos

Tren de 7

| $6 + 1$ | $5 + 2$ | $4 + 3$ |
| $1 + 6$ | $2 + 5$ | $3 + 4$ |

Usted verá los dibujos de los círculos y los trenes de partes en la tarea de matemáticas de su niño. Ayúdelo, si es necesario. Los niños están haciendo estas actividades en clase, pero es posible que aún así necesiten ayuda en casa.

Más adelante en la unidad se les presentarán a los niños los patrones. Trabajar con patrones ayuda a los niños a desarrollar la comprensión de la relación matemática. Aprenden a identificar, ampliar y completar los patrones que se repiten, aumentan y disminuyen. Pida a su niño que busque patrones diferentes a su alrededor. Por ejemplo, pueden hallar patrones en ropa, muebles o alfombras.

Si tiene preguntas o dudas, por favor comuníquese conmigo.

Atentamente,
El maestro de su niño

Write the partners.

1 5 = 4 + 1

5 = _____

5 = _____

5 = _____

2 4 = 3 + 1

4 = _____

4 = _____

3 3 = 2 + 1

3 = _____

4 2 = _____

5

6

Use **patterns** to solve.

VOCABULARY
patterns

7 2 + 0 = ☐   5 + 0 = ☐   3 + 0 = ☐

4 + 0 = ☐   1 + 0 = ☐   0 + 3 = ☐

0 + 5 = ☐   0 + 2 = ☐   0 + 4 = ☐

8 4 + 1 = ☐   2 + 1 = ☐   3 + 1 = ☐

1 + 1 = ☐   1 + 4 = ☐   1 + 3 = ☐

9 2 + 2 = ☐   3 + 2 = ☐   1 + 2 = ☐

10 2 − 0 = ☐   4 − 1 = ☐   3 − 2 = ☐

 Check Understanding

Make circle drawings for all the partners of 5.

© Houghton Mifflin Harcourt Publishing Company

Name _____

1 Show and write the 6-partners.

⬭ ○○○○○○   ___ + ___   6 = _____

⬭ ○○○○○○   ___ + ___   6 = _____

⬭ ○○○○○○   ___ + ___   6 = _____

⬭ ○○○○○○   ___ + ___   6 = _____

⬭ ○○○○○○   ___ + ___   6 = _____

2 Write the 6-partners.

3 Write the 6-partners as a train.

6-train

□ + □ + □ + □ + □

4 Discuss patterns in the partners.

2	3	4	5	6
1 + 1	2 + 1	3 + 1	4 + 1	5 + 1
		2 + 2	3 + 2	4 + 2
				3 + 3

Use **doubles** to solve.

5 $3 + 3 = \boxed{}$ $1 + 1 = \boxed{}$ $2 + 2 = \boxed{}$

$6 - 3 = \boxed{}$ $2 - 1 = \boxed{}$ $4 - 2 = \boxed{}$

Use patterns to solve.

6 $6 + 0 = \boxed{}$ $0 + 4 = \boxed{}$ $1 + 0 = \boxed{}$

7 $4 - 0 = \boxed{}$ $2 - 0 = \boxed{}$ $6 - 0 = \boxed{}$

8 $3 - 3 = \boxed{}$ $5 - 5 = \boxed{}$ $1 - 1 = \boxed{}$

$4 - 4 = \boxed{}$ $2 - 2 = \boxed{}$ $6 - 6 = \boxed{}$

✔ **Check Understanding**

Write all the partners of 6.

_____ + _____, _____ + _____, _____ + _____, _____ + _____, _____ + _____

Show the 7-partners and switch the partners.

1 ⬜ ○○○○○○○   _____ + _____   and   _____ + _____

2 ⬜ ○○○○○○○   _____ + _____   and   _____ + _____

3 ⬜ ○○○○○○○   _____ + _____   and   _____ + _____

Write the partners and the switched partners.

4 7-train

| _____ + _____ | _____ + _____ | _____ + _____ |
| _____ + _____ | _____ + _____ | _____ + _____ |

5

6 Discuss patterns in the partners.

2	3	4	5	6	7
1 + 1	2 + 1	3 + 1	4 + 1	5 + 1	6 + 1
		2 + 2	3 + 2	4 + 2	5 + 2
				3 + 3	4 + 3

Use patterns to solve.

7 3 + 1 = ☐   6 + 1 = ☐   4 + 1 = ☐

5 + 1 = ☐   2 + 1 = ☐   1 + 1 = ☐

8 1 + 2 = ☐   1 + 5 = ☐   1 + 4 = ☐

1 + 3 = ☐   1 + 6 = ☐   1 + 1 = ☐

9 7 − 1 = ☐   3 − 1 = ☐   5 − 1 = ☐

4 − 1 = ☐   6 − 1 = ☐   2 − 1 = ☐

10 5 − 4 = ☐   7 − 6 = ☐   3 − 2 = ☐

 Check Understanding

Explain the pattern you see when you switch the partners for 7.

Name _____

Show the 8-partners and switch the partners.

1. ○○○○○○○○ _____ + _____ and _____ + _____

2. ○○○○○○○○ _____ + _____ and _____ + _____

3. ○○○○○○○○ _____ + _____ and _____ + _____

4. ○○○○○○○○ _____ + _____ and _____ + _____

Write the partners and the switched partners.

5. 8-train

6.

7 Discuss patterns in the partners.

2	3	4	5	6	7	8
1 + 1	2 + 1	3 + 1	4 + 1	5 + 1	6 + 1	7 + 1
		2 + 2	3 + 2	4 + 2	5 + 2	6 + 2
				3 + 3	4 + 3	5 + 3
						4 + 4

Use doubles to solve.

8 4 + 4 = ☐   3 + 3 = ☐   2 + 2 = ☐

   8 − 4 = ☐   6 − 3 = ☐   4 − 2 = ☐

Use patterns to solve.

9 8 + 0 = ☐   6 + 0 = ☐   7 + 0 = ☐

10 7 − 0 = ☐   2 − 0 = ☐   8 − 0 = ☐

11 4 − 4 = ☐   6 − 6 = ☐   2 − 2 = ☐

✓ **Check Understanding**
Draw Math Mountains to show the partners for 8 and the switched partners.

Partners of 8

Name _____

Show the 9-partners and switch the partners.

1 ⬜ ○○○○○○○○○ ___ + ___ and ___ + ___

2 ⬜ ○○○○○○○○○ ___ + ___ and ___ + ___

3 ⬜ ○○○○○○○○○ ___ + ___ and ___ + ___

4 ⬜ ○○○○○○○○○ ___ + ___ and ___ + ___

Write the partners and the switched partners.

5 9-train

+	+	+	+
+	+	+	+

6

7 Discuss patterns in the partners.

2	**3**	**4**	**5**	**6**	**7**	**8**	**9**
1 + 1	2 + 1	3 + 1	4 + 1	5 + 1	6 + 1	7 + 1	8 + 1
	2 + 2	3 + 2	4 + 2	5 + 2	6 + 2	7 + 2
		3 + 3	4 + 3	5 + 3	6 + 3	7 + 3
			4 + 4	5 + 4	6 + 4	7 + 4

Use patterns to solve.

8 6 + 1 = ☐   8 + 1 = ☐

4 + 1 = ☐   3 + 1 = ☐

9 1 + 7 = ☐   1 + 2 = ☐

1 + 8 = ☐   1 + 4 = ☐

10 9 − 1 = ☐   3 − 1 = ☐

7 − 1 = ☐   6 − 1 = ☐

11 9 − 8 = ☐   3 − 2 = ☐

7 − 6 = ☐   6 − 5 = ☐

✔ **Check Understanding**

Write all the partners of 9 and the switched partners.

____ + ____ , ____ + ____ , ____ + ____ , ____ + ____

____ + ____ , ____ + ____ , ____ + ____ , ____ + ____

Name _____

1 Discuss patterns.

Partners of 10

●●●●● ●●●●○	●●●●● ●●●○○	●●●●● ●●○○○	●●●●● ●○○○○	●●●●● ○○○○○
9 + 1	8 + 2	7 + 3	6 + 4	5 + 5
1 + 9	2 + 8	3 + 7	4 + 6	

Write the 10-partners.

2

10 = 9 + 1

10 = 8 + 2

10 = _____

10 = _____

10 = _____

10 = _____

10 = _____

10 = _____

3

10

9 + 1

_____

_____

_____

_____

4 Discuss patterns.

Patterns with Partners

2	3	4	5	6	7	8	9	10
1 + 1	2 + 1	3 + 1	4 + 1	5 + 1	6 + 1	7 + 1	8 + 1	9 + 1
		2 + 2	3 + 2	4 + 2	5 + 2	6 + 2	7 + 2	8 + 2
				3 + 3	4 + 3	5 + 3	6 + 3	7 + 3
						4 + 4	5 + 4	6 + 4
								5 + 5

Patterns with Zero

1 + 0 = 1	1 − 0 = 1	1 − 1 = 0
2 + 0 = 2	2 − 0 = 2	2 − 2 = 0
3 + 0 = 3	3 − 0 = 3	3 − 3 = 0
4 + 0 = 4	4 − 0 = 4	4 − 4 = 0
5 + 0 = 5	5 − 0 = 5	5 − 5 = 0
6 + 0 = 6	6 − 0 = 6	6 − 6 = 0
7 + 0 = 7	7 − 0 = 7	7 − 7 = 0
8 + 0 = 8	8 − 0 = 8	8 − 8 = 0
9 + 0 = 9	9 − 0 = 9	9 − 9 = 0
10 + 0 = 10	10 − 0 = 10	10 − 10 = 0

Patterns with Doubles

1 + 1 = 2
2 + 2 = 4
3 + 3 = 6
4 + 4 = 8
5 + 5 = 10

✓ Check Understanding
Write the partners of 10 and the switched partners of 10.

© Houghton Mifflin Harcourt Publishing Company

Partners of 10

Write the number of band members in each column or row.

_____ _____ _____ _____ _____ _____ _____ _____

_____

_____

_____

_____

_____

_____

_____

_____

_____

_____

3 Show and write the partners of 10.

$10 =$ _____ $+$ _____

$10 =$ _____ $+$ _____

$10 =$ _____ $+$ _____

$10 =$ _____ $+$ _____

$10 =$ _____ $+$ _____

$10 =$ _____ $+$ _____

$10 =$ _____ $+$ _____

$10 =$ _____ $+$ _____

$10 =$ _____ $+$ _____

Focus on Problem Solving

Name _____   Date _____

Write two more partners for the number.

1 6 $\boxed{\bigcirc\bigcirc\bigcirc\bigcirc\bigcirc\bigcirc}$

$6 = 5 + 1$

$6 = $ _____

$6 = $ _____

2 8 $\boxed{\bigcirc\bigcirc\bigcirc\bigcirc\bigcirc\bigcirc\bigcirc\bigcirc}$

$8 = 7 + 1$

$8 = $ _____

$8 = $ _____

Use doubles or patterns to solve.

3 $0 + 4 = \boxed{}$

4 $4 + 4 = \boxed{}$

5 $7 - 0 = \boxed{}$

Name _____ Date _____

1 Write the partners.

2 Choose a set of 9-partners. Write or draw a story about the 9-partners.

VOCABULARY
repeating pattern

Ring the part of the pattern that repeats.
Label the pattern AB, ABCD, or AAB.

1   label: _____

2   label: _____

3 T B Y K T B Y K T B Y K   label: _____

4   label: _____

Extend the **repeating pattern**.
Draw the fruit.

5   ____ ____

6   ____ ____

7   ____ ____

8   ____ ____

Complete the pattern.

9

10

11

12

13 Use numbers to create the same type of repeating pattern as problem 9.

14 Draw shapes to create an AB repeating pattern.

✓ **Check Understanding**
Draw a repeating pattern using this group of shapes.

© Houghton Mifflin Harcourt Publishing Company

Repeating Patterns

Name _____

Continue each **growing pattern** two more times.

1

____ ____

2

_____ _____

3 AB   ABB   ABBB   _____ _____

Complete the pattern. Write the pattern rule.

4
454
44544
4445444
444454444

_____

444444544444 4

rule: _____

5 Create a growing pattern with shapes.

Count by 2s to complete the pattern.

 1, 3, 5, _____ , _____

 4, 6, 8, _____

Continue each **shrinking pattern** two more times.

9 ACCCCC   ACCCC   ACCC   _____ _____

Complete the pattern. Write the pattern rule.

10

rule: _____

✓ **Check Understanding**

What is the pattern rule for Problem 8?

rule: _____

1 Ring the part of the pattern that repeats.

2 Draw a shape to complete the pattern.

3 Count by 2s to complete the pattern.

2, 4, 6, _____

4 Complete the pattern. Write the pattern rule.

XXXXXX
XXXXX
XXXX
XXX
_____

rule: _____

5 Continue the pattern two times.

Name _____

Date _____

Add.

1 $1 + 0 = \boxed{}$ **2** $0 + 3 = \boxed{}$ **3** $9 + 0 = \boxed{}$

4 $0 + 2 = \boxed{}$ **5** $4 + 0 = \boxed{}$ **6** $5 + 0 = \boxed{}$

7 $7 + 0 = \boxed{}$ **8** $0 + 9 = \boxed{}$ **9** $8 + 0 = \boxed{}$

10 $0 + 6 = \boxed{}$ **11** $2 + 0 = \boxed{}$ **12** $10 + 0 = \boxed{}$

13 $0 + 1 = \boxed{}$ **14** $3 + 0 = \boxed{}$ **15** $0 + 7 = \boxed{}$

See the 5-group.
Draw extra dots to show the number.

1 7

2 8

3 Does the picture match the number?
Choose Yes or No.

7

○ Yes   ○ No

4 Continue the pattern two more times.

5 Extend the pattern.

H H Y H H Y H H Y ____

6 Choose all the 10-partners.

○ 2 + 8

○ 3 + 5

○ 8 + 3

○ 8 + 2

---

7 Complete the 6-partners.

6 = 5 +
| 1 |
| 2 |
| 3 |

6 = 4 +
| 0 |
| 1 |
| 2 |

6 =
| 0 |
| 1 |
| 2 |
+ 6

---

8 Write the numbers in the boxes to show the partners.

| 1 | 2 | 3 | 4 | 5 | 6 | 7 | 8 |

---

9 Use patterns to solve.

6 + 1 = ☐   5 + 1 = ☐   4 + 1 = ☐

Write the partners.

⑩   5 = _____ + _____

⑪   7 = _____ + _____

⑫   6 = _____ + _____

⑬ Write facts that match each total.

| 8 + 1 | 9 + 0 | 6 + 1 | 4 + 4 | 7 + 0 | 1 + 7 |

7	8	9

Write the partners and the switched partners.

⑭   [___ + ___] and [___ + ___]

⑮   [___ + ___] and [___ + ___]

⑯   [___ + ___] and [___ + ___]

17 Use patterns to solve.

$3 - 1 = \boxed{}$

$4 - 1 = \boxed{}$

$5 - 1 = \boxed{}$

18 Draw a story about a set of 8-partners.
Write the partners.

Plant Flowers

1 Draw 5 flowers growing in the pot.
Make some red. Make some yellow.

2 Write the 5-partners the flowers show.
Then switch the partners.

3 Draw 10 flowers growing in the pot.
Make some blue. Make some yellow.

4 Write the 10-partners the flowers show.
Then switch the partners.

5 Can you show 10 with blue and yellow flowers
in other ways? Tell why or why not.

_____

_____

Color Plates

6 Draw 9 plates. Make some red. Make some blue.

7 Write the 9-partners that the plates show.
Then switch the partners.

---

8 Color the plates below yellow. Then draw blue
plates to make 10 plates in all.

9 Write the 10-partners the plates show.
Then switch the partners.

10 Can you show another number of blue plates to
add to the yellow plates to make 10 in all?
Tell why or why not.

_____

_____

Dear Family:

Your child has started a new unit on addition, subtraction, and equations. These concepts are introduced with stories that capture children's interest and help them to see adding and subtracting as real-life processes.

At the beginning of the unit, children show a story problem by drawing a picture of the objects. If they are adding 4 balloons and 2 balloons, for example, their pictures might look like the top one shown here. If they are subtracting, their pictures might look like the bottom one.

Addition

Subtraction

In a short time, children will show objects quickly with circles rather than pictures. This is a major conceptual advance because it requires the use of symbols. Children are asked to show the partners (4 + 2) as well as give the total (6). From here, children are just a small step away from writing standard equations, such as 4 + 2 = 6 and 6 − 4 = 2.

Addition Problem

Subtraction Problem

To keep them focused on the actual problem, children are often asked to give a "complete answer" in class. This means that they should name the objects as well as give the number. Right now, complete answers are not required for homework. Even so, it would be helpful for you to ask your child to say the complete answer when working with you at home. Example: "You said the answer is 6. Is it 6 dinosaurs? No? Then 6 what? . . . Oh! 6 balloons!"

Sincerely,
Your child's teacher

Estimada familia:

Su niño ha empezado una nueva unidad sobre la suma, la resta y las ecuaciones. Estos conceptos se presentan con cuentos que captan el interés de los niños y les ayudan a ver la suma y la resta como procesos de la vida diaria.

Al comienzo de la unidad, los niños muestran un problema en forma de cuento haciendo un dibujo de los objetos. Por ejemplo, si están sumando 4 globos y 2 globos, sus dibujos pueden parecerse al dibujo de arriba. Si están restando, es posible que sus dibujos se parezcan al dibujo de abajo.

Suma

Al poco tiempo, los niños mostrarán objetos rápidamente con círculos en vez de dibujos. Esto es un gran paso conceptual, ya que requiere el uso de signos. A los niños se les pide que muestren las partes (4 + 2) y la respuesta (6). Una vez que hacen esto, están casi listos para escribir ecuaciones normales, tales como $4 + 2 = 6$ y $6 - 4 = 2$.

Resta

$4 + 2$

○○○○|○○

6

Problema de suma

$6 - 4$

~~○○○○~~|○○

2

Problema de resta

Para que sigan concentrándose en el problema mismo, a los niños se les pide una "respuesta completa" en la clase. Esto significa que deben nombrar los objetos y dar el número. Actualmente, no se requieren respuestas completas en la tarea. Sin embargo, sería de ayuda si le pidiera a su niño que le dé la respuesta completa cuando trabaja con Ud. en casa. Por ejemplo: "Dijiste que la respuesta es 6. ¿Son 6 dinosaurios? ¿No? Entonces, ¿6 de qué?. . . ¡Ajá! ¡6 globos!"

Atentamente,
El maestro de su niño

cent

nickel

count on

penny

equation

subtract

front   back

5 cents or 5¢

The number of **cents** is the value of a set of coins.

7 cents

front   back

1 cent or 1¢

$5 + 4 = \boxed{9}$

$5 + \boxed{4} = 9$

$9 - 5 = \boxed{4}$

5
  6 7 8 9

Count on from 5 to get the answer.

$8 - 3 = 5$

◯ ◯ ◯ ◯ ◯ ◯ ◯ ◯

$4 + 3 = 7$ $7 = 4 + 3$

$9 - 5 = 4$ $4 = 9 - 5$

total

vertical form

$$4 + 3 = 7 \qquad \begin{array}{r} 4 \\ +\ 3 \\ \hline 7 \end{array}$$

total →

$$\begin{array}{r} 6 \\ +\ 3 \\ \hline 9 \end{array} \qquad \begin{array}{r} 9 \\ -\ 3 \\ \hline 6 \end{array}$$

Name _____

VOCABULARY
total

Write the partners and the **total**.

1 ☐ + ☐

Total ☐

2 ☐ + ☐

Total ☐

3 ☐ + ☐

Total ☐

4 ☐ + ☐

Total ☐

5 ☐ + ☐

Total ☐

6 ☐ + ☐

Total ☐

7 Draw a picture of flowers to show 4 + 2. Write the total.

Represent Addition **49**

Write the partners and the total.

8

Total ☐

---

9 ☐ + ☐

Total ☐

---

10 ☐ + ☐

Total ☐

✔ **Check Understanding**

Listen to the math story. Then draw it and write the partners and the total.

Represent Addition

Name _____

Write the partners and total for each circle drawing.

1

Total

2

Total

3

Total

4

Total

5

Total

6

Total

7 Make a circle drawing to show 5 + 5.

Match the pictures to the circle drawings.

8

Total

9

Total

10

Total

✓ **Check Understanding**

Use the circle drawing to tell a math story. Explain how to use the circles to represent the story.

Addition with Circle Drawings

Name _____

Write the partners and the total. Then write the **equation**.

Total [ ]

_____
Equation

②

Total [ ]

_____
Equation

③

Total [ ]

_____
Equation

④

Total [ ]

_____
Equation

⑤ Write an equation of your own. _____

Write the partners and the total. Then write the equation.

6

Total ☐

_____
Equation

7

Total ☐

_____
Equation

 Add.

1 $1 + 0 =$ ☐   **2** $0 + 8 =$ ☐   **3** $6 + 0 =$ ☐

 Check Understanding

Write an equation with numbers on each
side of an equal sign. ____ + ____ = ____

Addition Equations

Make a circle drawing for the story problem.
Write the equation.

1 There are 4 elephants drinking from the river. Then 2 more elephants join them. How many elephants are there in all?

_____
Equation

2 Teresa plants 5 roses in the garden. Hugo plants 4 roses. How many roses did they plant in all?

_____
Equation

3 Henry played 6 outside games last week. Then he played 3 computer games. How many games did he play altogether?

_____
Equation

Circle if the equation is true or false.
Draw a line to change = to ≠ if it is false.
Draw to explain.

4 $2 + 3 = 3 + 2$

true   false

5 $6 + 1 = 5 + 1$

true   false

6 $4 + 4 = 7 + 2$

true   false

7 $3 + 2 = 1 + 4$

true   false

✓ **Check Understanding**

Complete the equation to make it true.

$3 + 4 = 5 +$ ☐

© Houghton Mifflin Harcourt Publishing Company

Addition Equations and Stories

Name _____ Date _____

Write the partners and the total.

1

Total ☐

2

Total ☐

Write the partners and total.

3 +

Total ☐

4 ☐ + ☐

Total ☐

Write a true equation for the story.

5 There are 7 plates on the table.
Anna puts 3 more plates on the table.
How many plates are on the table now?

_____

Name _____   Date _____

Add.

1 $2 + 0 =$ ☐   **2** $0 + 4 =$ ☐   **3** $7 + 0 =$ ☐

4 $0 + 1 =$ ☐   **5** $3 + 0 =$ ☐   **6** $0 + 5 =$ ☐

7 $9 + 0 =$ ☐   **8** $0 + 8 =$ ☐   **9** $6 + 0 =$ ☐

10 $0 + 10 =$ ☐   **11** $5 + 0 =$ ☐   **12** $0 + 7 =$ ☐

13 $8 + 0 =$ ☐   **14** $0 + 9 =$ ☐   **15** $10 + 0 =$ ☐

Dear Family:

Earlier in the unit, your child solved addition problems by making math drawings and counting every object. This is called *counting all*. Now your child is learning a faster strategy that allows them to work directly with numbers. The method they are learning is called *counting on*. It is explained below.

In an addition problem such as 5 + 4, children say (or "think") the first number as if they had already counted it. Then they count on from there. The last number they say is the total. Children can keep track by raising a finger or making a dot for each number as they count on. The diagram below shows both the finger method and the dot method.

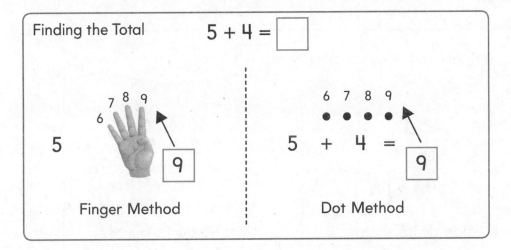

In this unit children are introduced to pennies and nickels. They apply the Counting On strategy as they count coins to find the total amount of cents.

Counting on requires repeated practice. This is provided in class activities and homework assignments. Right now, your child is learning how to find unknown totals. In the next unit, he or she will learn to use the Counting On strategy to subtract.

Counting on is a temporary method to help children build fluency with addition and subtraction within 10. The goal by the end of the grade is for children to automatically know the answer when the total is 10 or less.

Sincerely,
Your child's teacher

Estimada familia:

Un poco antes en la unidad su niño resolvió problemas de suma haciendo dibujos matemáticos y contando todos los objetos. A esto se le llama *contar todo*. Ahora su niño está aprendiendo una estrategia más rápida que le permite trabajar directamente con los números. El método que está aprendiendo se llama *contar hacia adelante*. Se explica a continuación.

En un problema de suma, como 5 + 4, los niños dicen (o "piensan") el primer número como si ya lo hubieran contado. Luego cuentan hacia adelante a partir de él. El último número que dicen es el total. Los niños pueden llevar la cuenta levantando un dedo o haciendo un punto por cada número mientras cuentan hacia adelante. El diagrama a continuación muestra tanto el método de los dedos como el de los puntos.

En esta unidad se les presentarán a los niños las monedas de un centavo y de cinco centavos. Aplicarán la estrategia de contar hacia adelante mientras cuentan las monedas para hallar la cantidad total de centavos.

Contar hacia adelante requiere práctica. Esto sucede en las actividades de clase y tareas. En esta unidad, su niño está aprendiendo a hallar un total desconocido. En la próxima unidad, aprenderá a usar la estrategia de contar hacia adelante para restar.

Contar hacia adelante es un método que sirve como ayuda para que los niños dominen la suma y la resta en operaciones hasta el 10. La meta es lograr que al final del año escolar sepan automáticamente la respuesta cuando el total sea 10 ó menos.

Atentamente,
El maestro de su niño

Explore Solution Methods

Name _____

Count on. Write the total.

① 5 + 2 = ☐

5

② 6 + 4 = ☐

6

③ 8 + 1 = ☐

8

④ 3 + 5 = ☐

3

⑤ 7 + 3 = ☐

7

⑥ 2 + 2 = ☐

2

⑦ 4 + 5 = ☐

4

⑧ 9 + 1 = ☐

9

⑨ 3 + 2 = ☐

3

⑩ 5 + 1 = ☐

5

11 Solve.

7 + 2 = ☐

Draw or write to explain how to count on.

> (empty box)

Draw or write a different way to solve.

> (empty box)

---

12 Choose a number 1, 2, 3, 4, or 5. Count on 3 more. Complete the equation. Draw or write to explain.

 + 3 = ☐

 Check Understanding

Explain if you would use counting all or counting on to solve 5 + 3 = ☐.

Explore Solution Methods

Name _____

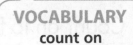

VOCABULARY
count on

Count on to find the total.

① 4 + 3 = ☐   ② 6 + 4 = ☐   ③ 6 + 2 = ☐

④ 4 + 5 = ☐   ⑤ 5 + 3 = ☐   ⑥ 8 + 2 = ☐

⑦ 2 + 3 = ☐   ⑧ 7 + 3 = ☐   ⑨ 4 + 2 = ☐

Find the total number of toys.

⑩ 3 cars in the box

☐ Total

⑪ 7 boats in the box

☐ Total

⑫ 6 dolls in the box

☐ Total

⑬ 5 balls in the box

☐ Total

⑭ Write an equation that shows a total of 10. _____

Addition Strategies: Counting On **63**

Count on to find the total.

⑮ 6 + 3 = ☐   ⑯ 5 + 2 = ☐   ⑰ 7 + 2 = ☐

⑱ 7 + 3 = ☐   ⑲ 4 + 3 = ☐   ⑳ 4 + 5 = ☐

㉑ 8 + 2 = ☐   ㉒ 5 + 2 = ☐   ㉓ 4 + 2 = ☐

㉔ 5 + 3 = ☐   ㉕ 7 + 2 = ☐   ㉖ 7 + 3 = ☐

㉗ 6 + 2 = ☐   ㉘ 6 + 4 = ☐   ㉙ 3 + 4 = ☐

(PATH to FLUENCY) **Add.**

① 7 + 0 = ☐   ② 1 + 8 = ☐   ③ 0 + 8 = ☐

④ 9 + 0 = ☐   ⑤ 7 + 1 = ☐   ⑥ 10 + 0 = ☐

⑦ 6 + 1 = ☐   ⑧ 8 + 0 = ☐   ⑨ 8 + 1 = ☐

✔ **Check Understanding**

Draw dots to show how to count on

to solve 6 + 4 = ☐.

Addition Strategies: Counting On

Name _____

Underline the greater number.
Count on from that number.

① 3 + <u>7</u> = ☐

② 4 + 5 = ☐

③ 2 + 6 = ☐

④ 5 + 3 = ☐

⑤ 7 + 2 = ☐

⑥ 3 + 6 = ☐

⑦ 5 + 2 = ☐

⑧ 2 + 8 = ☐

⑨ 7 + 3 = ☐

⑩ 6 + 3 = ☐

⑪ Show two ways to count on to find the total
of 6 + 3. Which is faster?

Underline the greater number.
Count on from that number.

⑫ <u>5</u> + 2 = ☐

⑬ 7 + 3 = ☐

⑭ 6 + 2 = ☐

⑮ 5 + 3 = ☐

⑯ 3 + 4 = ☐

⑰ 2 + 7 = ☐

⑱ 6 + 3 = ☐

⑲ 8 + 2 = ☐

⑳ 4 + 3 = ☐

㉑ 2 + 5 = ☐

㉒ 4 + 6 = ☐

㉓ 3 + 7 = ☐

㉔ How did you solve Exercise 17?

☐

© Houghton Mifflin Harcourt Publishing Company

Count On from the Greater Number

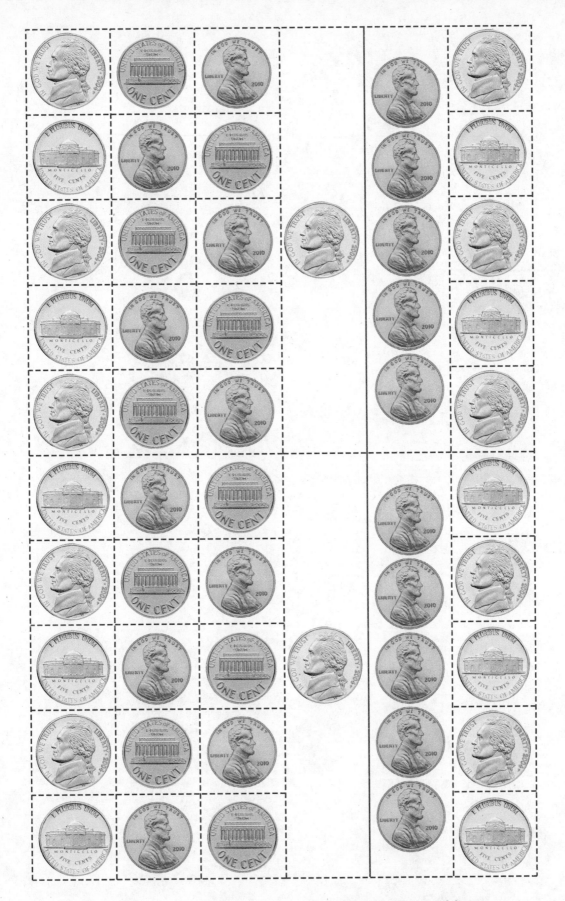

Cut on the dotted lines.
Fold on the solid lines.

Nickel Strips and Coins **67**

Nickel Strips and Coins

Name _____

Look at the groups of **nickels** and **pennies**.
Write how many **cents** in each group.

25

[ ] ¢

26

[ ] ¢

27

[ ] ¢

28

[ ] ¢

29

[ ] ¢

30

[ ] ¢

Count On from the Greater Number **69**

Count the coins. Match.

31   •   • 4¢

32   •   • 6¢

33   •   • 7¢

34   •   • 9¢

35   •   • 8¢

✓ **Check Understanding**

To use counting on to solve $4 + 5 = \boxed{}$,

which number would you start with? Why?

Count On from the Greater Number

$3 + 3 = \boxed{}$

$3 + 4 = \boxed{}$

$3 + 5 = \boxed{}$

$3 + 6 = \boxed{}$

$3 + 7 = \boxed{}$

$4 + 3 = \boxed{}$

$4 + 4 = \boxed{}$

$4 + 5 = \boxed{}$

$4 + 6 = \boxed{}$

$5 + 3 = \boxed{}$

$5 + 4 = \boxed{}$

$5 + 5 = \boxed{}$

$6 + 3 = \boxed{}$

$6 + 4 = \boxed{}$

$7 + 3 = \boxed{}$

$3 + 5 = \boxed{8}$

$\boxed{\cdots \mid 5}$

$3 + 4 = \boxed{7}$

$\boxed{\cdots \mid 4}$

$3 + 3 = \boxed{6}$

$\boxed{3 \mid \cdots}$

$4 + 3 = \boxed{7}$

$\boxed{4 \mid \cdots}$

$3 + 7 = \boxed{10}$

$\boxed{\cdots \mid 7}$

$3 + 6 = \boxed{9}$

$\boxed{\cdots \mid 6}$

$4 + 6 = \boxed{10}$

$\boxed{\cdots\cdot \mid 6}$

$4 + 5 = \boxed{9}$

$\boxed{\cdots\cdot \mid 5}$

$4 + 4 = \boxed{8}$

$\boxed{4 \mid \cdots\cdot}$

$5 + 5 = \boxed{10}$

$\boxed{5 \mid \cdots\cdot\cdot}$

$5 + 4 = \boxed{9}$

$\boxed{5 \mid \cdots\cdot}$

$5 + 3 = \boxed{8}$

$\boxed{5 \mid \cdots}$

$7 + 3 = \boxed{10}$

$\boxed{7 \mid \cdots}$

$6 + 4 = \boxed{10}$

$\boxed{6 \mid \cdots\cdot}$

$6 + 3 = \boxed{9}$

$\boxed{6 \mid \cdots}$

Red Count-On Cards

Number Quilt 1: Unknown Totals

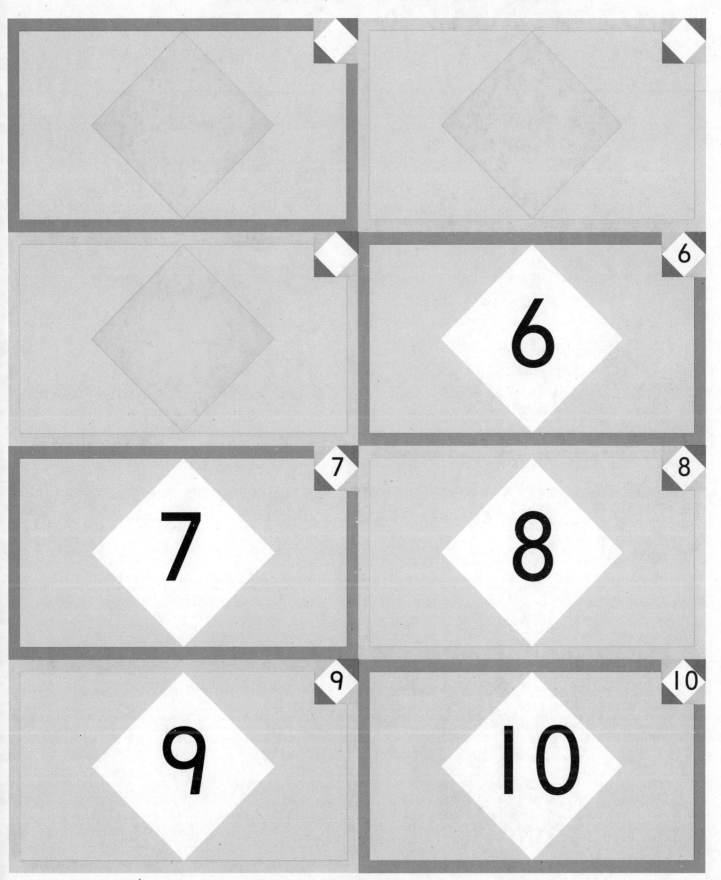

Use with Red Count-On Cards.

Number Quilt 1

Draw more to count on. Write how many in all.

1) $4 + 1 = \boxed{}$

2) $6 + 2 = \boxed{}$

3) $3 + 3 = \boxed{}$

4) $5 + 4 = \boxed{}$

5) $7 + 3 = \boxed{}$

Underline the greater number.
Count on from that number.

6 2 + <u>8</u> = ☐   **7** 5 + 4 = ☐   **8** 6 + 3 = ☐

9 7 + 3 = ☐   **10** 2 + 5 = ☐   **11** 3 + 4 = ☐

12 4 + 3 = ☐   **13** 2 + 7 = ☐   **14** 8 + 2 = ☐

15 3 + 6 = ☐   **16** 5 + 2 = ☐   **17** 6 + 2 = ☐

18 5 + 3 = ☐   **19** 4 + 5 = ☐   **20** 2 + 6 = ☐

PATH to FLUENCY Add.

1 3 + 2 = ☐   **2** 1 + 9 = ☐   **3** 7 + 0 = ☐

4 8 + 1 = ☐   **5** 0 + 9 = ☐   **6** 1 + 6 = ☐

7 8 + 0 = ☐   **8** 7 + 1 = ☐   **9** 2 + 3 = ☐

✓ **Check Understanding**

Explain how to count on to solve 6 + 3 = ☐ and
2 + 8 = ☐.

Addition Games: Unknown Totals

Name _____

Write the addition equation the model shows.

1

_____
Equation

2

_____
Equation

3

_____
Equation

4

_____
Equation

5

_____
Equation

Underline the greater addend in the equation.
Count on from that number and write the total.

6 $6 + 3 =$ ⬜

| 6 | ● ● ● |

7 $2 + 5 =$ ⬜

| ● ● | 5 |

8 $7 + 3 =$ ⬜

| 7 | ● ● ● |

9 $5 + 3 =$ ⬜

| 5 | ● ● ● |

10 $2 + 4 =$ ⬜

| ● ● | 4 |

11 $4 + 5 =$ ⬜

| ● ● ● ● | 5 |

12 $3 + 7 =$ ⬜

| ● ● ● | 7 |

13 $6 + 2 =$ ⬜

| 6 | ● ● |

14 $4 + 6 =$ ⬜

| ● ● ● ● | 6 |

15 $7 + 2 =$ ⬜

| 7 | ● ● |

✓ **Check Understanding**

Draw circles to show counting on to solve
$4 + 3 =$ ⬜ and $2 + 7 =$ ⬜.

Practice Counting On

Count on to find the total.

① 3 + 2 = ☐

② Write how many cents.

☐ ¢

Underline the greater number.
Count on from that number.

③ 4 + 5 = ☐

④ 6 + 3 = ☐

⑤ Draw more to count on.
Write how many in all.

○○○○○

5 + 2 = ☐

Name _____   Date _____

PATH to
FLUENCY

Add.

1 5 + 0 = ☐   **2** 0 + 6 = ☐   **3** 0 + 8 = ☐

4 9 + 0 = ☐   **5** 0 + 10 = ☐   **6** 9 + 1 = ☐

7 1 + 3 = ☐   **8** 2 + 1 = ☐   **9** 2 + 3 = ☐

10 1 + 5 = ☐   **11** 4 + 0 = ☐   **12** 7 + 1 = ☐

13 3 + 2 = ☐   **14** 1 + 9 = ☐   **15** 8 + 1 = ☐

Name _____

Solve. Write how many are left.

1   There are 8 apples.

$8 - 5 =$ ☐

Then 5 are eaten.

2   There are 9 flowers.

$9 - 4 =$ ☐

Then 4 are picked.

3   There are 6 dolphins.

$6 - 3 =$ ☐

Then 3 swim away.

4   There are 10 balloons.

$10 - 6 =$ ☐

Then 6 pop.

5 You have 7 balls. You lose 2 balls. How many balls are left? Solve. Show your work.

Represent Subtraction **81**

Solve. Write how many are left.

6   There are 10 balloons.

$10 - 4 =$ ☐

Then 4 pop.

---

7   There are 8 apples.

$8 - 6 =$ ☐

Then 6 are eaten.

---

8 Look at Puzzled Penguin's work.

There were 7 flowers.

Then 3 were picked.

$7 - 3 = \boxed{3}$

Am I correct?

Help Puzzled Penguin.

✓ **Check Understanding**
Draw circles to solve
$8 - 2 =$ ☐.

© Houghton Mifflin Harcourt Publishing Company

Represent Subtraction

Name _____

VOCABULARY
subtract

Subtract and write the equation.

1
Subtract 5

○○○○○ ○○○○

_____
Equation
_____

2
Subtract 4

○○○○○ ○○○○○

_____
Equation
_____

3
Subtract 3

○○○○○ ○○

_____
Equation
_____

4
Subtract 8

○○○○○ ○○○○○

_____
Equation
_____

5
Subtract 5

○○○○○ ○○○

_____
Equation
_____

6
Subtract 7

○○○○○ ○○○○○

_____
Equation
_____

7
Subtract 6

○○○○○ ○○○○

_____
Equation
_____

Subtract and write the equation.

8   Subtract 5

_____ Equation

9   Subtract 3

_____ Equation

10   Subtract 6

_____ Equation

11   Subtract 4

_____ Equation

12   Subtract 2

_____ Equation

13 There are 6 toy trucks on the table. 4 trucks roll off. How many toy trucks are there now? Use a circle drawing to solve. Then write the equation.

✔ **Check Understanding**
Make a circle drawing to show $10 - 7 = 3$.

Subtraction with Drawings and Equations

Name _____

Use the picture to solve the equation.

1 ⓞⓞⓞⓞⓞ ⓞⓞⓞⓞ

$$9 - 6 = \boxed{}$$

2 ⓞⓞⓞⓞⓞ ⓞⓞⓞ

$$8 - 5 = \boxed{}$$

3 ⓞⓞⓞⓞ

$$4 - 4 = \boxed{}$$

4 ⓞⓞⓞⓞⓞ ⓞⓞ

$$7 - 3 = \boxed{}$$

5 ⓞⓞⓞⓞⓞ ⓞ

$$6 - 5 = \boxed{}$$

6 ⓞⓞⓞⓞⓞ

$$5 - 4 = \boxed{}$$

7 ⓞⓞⓞⓞⓞ ⓞⓞⓞⓞⓞ

$$10 - 6 = \boxed{}$$

8 ⓞⓞⓞⓞⓞ ⓞⓞⓞⓞ

$$9 - 3 = \boxed{}$$

9 ⓞⓞⓞⓞⓞ ⓞⓞ

$$7 - 6 = \boxed{}$$

10 ⓞⓞⓞⓞⓞ ⓞⓞⓞⓞⓞ

$$10 - 2 = \boxed{}$$

11 ⓞⓞⓞⓞⓞ ⓞⓞⓞ

$$8 - 4 = \boxed{}$$

12 ⓞⓞⓞⓞⓞ ⓞ

$$6 - 2 = \boxed{}$$

Use the picture to solve the equation.

⑬

$5 - 3 = \boxed{}$

⑭

$7 - 4 = \boxed{}$

⑮

$9 - 5 = \boxed{}$

⑯

$6 - 4 = \boxed{}$

⑰

$10 - 3 = \boxed{}$

⑱

$8 - 6 = \boxed{}$

⑲ Make a circle drawing for the equation $6 - 2 = \boxed{}$. Then find the answer.

PATH to FLUENCY **Subtract.**

① $2 - 1 = \boxed{}$ ② $6 - 0 = \boxed{}$ ③ $1 - 0 = \boxed{}$

④ $4 - 1 = \boxed{}$ ⑤ $3 - 1 = \boxed{}$ ⑥ $10 - 0 = \boxed{}$

✓ Check Understanding

Listen to the story. Write and solve the equation for the story.

Practice with Subtraction

Write the equation for the story problem. Draw circles to prove if the equation is true or false.

1 There are 8 people at the party.
Then 2 people leave. Now there are
6 people at the party.

_____ Equation

2 There are 6 cups on the table.
Tim puts 3 cups in the dishwasher.
Now there are 2 cups on the table.

_____ Equation

3 There are 7 birds in the tree. 4 fly away.
Now there are 4 birds in the tree.

_____ Equation

Circle if the equation is true or false.
Draw to explain.

4 $9 - 4 = 7 - 1$

true   false

5 $6 - 3 = 8 - 5$

true   false

6 $4 - 1 = 5 - 2$

true   false

7 $7 - 2 = 9 - 4$

true   false

8 $3 - 1 = 4 - 1$

true   false

9 $6 - 3 = 8 - 6$

true   false

 Check Understanding

Make a circle drawing to show $9 - 6 = \boxed{}$.

Generate Subtraction Problems

Name _____   Date _____

Write how many are left.

Use the picture to help you.

1 There are 7 fish.

Then 3 swim away.

$7 - 3 =$ ☐

---

2 There are 10 snails.

Then 5 crawl away.

$10 - 5 =$ ☐

Use the picture to solve the equation.

3

$7 - 5 =$ ☐

Subtract and write the equation.

4

Subtract 4

_____
Equation

5

Subtract 6

_____
Equation

PATH to FLUENCY

Subtract.

1 $1 - 0 = \boxed{}$ **2** $3 - 1 = \boxed{}$ **3** $2 - 0 = \boxed{}$

4 $4 - 1 = \boxed{}$ **5** $6 - 0 = \boxed{}$ **6** $5 - 1 = \boxed{}$

7 $7 - 0 = \boxed{}$ **8** $8 - 1 = \boxed{}$ **9** $9 - 1 = \boxed{}$

10 $8 - 0 = \boxed{}$ **11** $9 - 0 = \boxed{}$ **12** $7 - 1 = \boxed{}$

13 $10 - 0 = \boxed{}$ **14** $6 - 1 = \boxed{}$ **15** $10 - 1 = \boxed{}$

Name _____

Relate addition and subtraction.

1

Addition	Subtraction
5 cats are here.	8 cats are here.
3 cats come.	5 cats run away.
How many cats in all?	How many cats are left?
$5 + 3 = $ ●●●●● | ○○○	$8 - 5 = $ ●●●●● ○○○
$5 + 3 = \square$	$8 - 5 = \square$
$5 + 3 = \boxed{}$	$8 - 5 = \boxed{}$
Total Unknown	Partner Unknown
	$5 + \square = 8$

Use addition to solve subtraction.

2 $4 + 4 = 8$, so I know $8 - 4 = \boxed{}$.

3 $6 + 3 = 9$, so I know $9 - 6 = \boxed{}$.

4 $7 + 3 = 10$, so I know $10 - 7 = \boxed{}$.

5 $5 + 4 = 9$, so I know $9 - 5 = \boxed{}$.

6 $3 + 3 = 6$, so I know $6 - 3 = \boxed{}$.

Equations	Vertical Forms	
$5 + 3 = 8$	5	8
$8 - 5 = 3$	$\underline{+\ 3}$	$\underline{-\ 5}$
	8	3

Solve the **vertical form**. Use any method.

7　　6
　　$\underline{+\ 4}$

8　　7
　　$\underline{+\ 2}$

9　　1
　　$\underline{+\ 6}$

10　　2
　　$\underline{+\ 6}$

11　　3
　　$\underline{+\ 7}$

Solve the vertical form. Think about addition.

12　　10
　　$\underline{-\ 8}$

13　　9
　　$\underline{-\ 5}$

14　　7
　　$\underline{-\ 1}$

15　　8
　　$\underline{-\ 3}$

16　　10
　　$\underline{-\ 5}$

PATH to FLUENCY Subtract.

1 $4 - 0 = \boxed{}$

2 $6 - 1 = \boxed{}$

3 $4 - 2 = \boxed{}$

4 $9 - 1 = \boxed{}$

5 $5 - 2 = \boxed{}$

6 $8 - 0 = \boxed{}$

7 $3 - 2 = \boxed{}$

8 $9 - 0 = \boxed{}$

9 $7 - 1 = \boxed{}$

Check Understanding

Write the related subtraction equation for
$5 + 4 = 9$. Write the vertical form.

Relate Addition and Subtraction

Name _____

Date _____

Use addition to solve subtraction.

1 $5 + 3 = 8$, so I know $8 - 3 = \boxed{}$.

2 $6 + 4 = 10$, so I know $10 - 4 = \boxed{}$.

Solve the vertical form.
Think about addition.

3
$$\begin{array}{r} 6 \\ -\,2 \\ \hline \end{array}$$

4
$$\begin{array}{r} 8 \\ -\,1 \\ \hline \end{array}$$

5
$$\begin{array}{r} 9 \\ -\,7 \\ \hline \end{array}$$

Name _____   Date _____

Subtract.

1 1 − 1 = ☐   **2** 2 − 0 = ☐   **3** 2 − 1 = ☐

4 4 − 1 = ☐   **5** 3 − 1 = ☐   **6** 5 − 0 = ☐

7 3 − 2 = ☐   **8** 5 − 1 = ☐   **9** 6 − 0 = ☐

10 7 − 0 = ☐   **11** 4 − 2 = ☐   **12** 6 − 1 = ☐

13 8 − 1 = ☐   **14** 9 − 0 = ☐   **15** 5 − 2 = ☐

Write the partners and the total.

Total [ ]

Total

3. Does the equation match the circle drawing?
Choose Yes or No.

$3 + 2 = 5$

○ Yes   ○ No

$5 + 2 = 7$

○ Yes   ○ No

$6 + 3 = 9$

○ Yes   ○ No

Ring the total number of toys in the group.

4 7 dolls in the box

7
9
0 Total

5 Write how many cents.

      ☐ ¢

6 Ring a number to show the cars in the box. Write the total.

4
5
6

☐ Total

7 Solve. Match the story or circle drawing to the equation.

There are 8 apples.

•

• $9 - 3 = 6$

Then 3 are eaten.

There are 7 flowers.

•

• $10 - 6 = 4$

Then 5 are picked.

Subtract 3

                                        •

• $7 - 5 = 2$

Subtract 6

                                        •

• $8 - 3 = 5$

8 Make a circle drawing

for the equation $6 - 4 = \boxed{}$.

Then find the answer.

9 Write the subtraction equation below the addition equation that helps you solve it.

$10 - 2 = 8$	$8 - 5 = 3$	$9 - 4 = 5$
$3 + 5 = 8$	$5 + 4 = 9$	$8 + 2 = 10$

_____   _____   _____

10 Write an equation for the story. Make a
Proof Drawing to show that the equation is true.
Write the vertical form.

There are 7 flowers in the vase.

Lily puts 2 more flowers in the vase.

Now there are 9 flowers.

How Many?

1 Take some red cubes.
Write the number of red cubes. _____

2 Take some blue cubes.
Write the number of blue cubes. _____

3 Draw to show the red cubes and blue cubes.

4 Write an equation that shows how many cubes in all.

_____ + _____ = _____

5 Tell how you added the cubes.

_____

_____

6 Write a subtraction equation.
Make a Proof Drawing to solve it.

_____ − _____ = _____

7 Tell how you subtracted the circles.

_____

_____

8 **Part A**

Write an addition story.

_____

_____

Part B

Write an equation to show your addition story.
Make a Proof Drawing of your addition story.

____ + ____ = ____

Tell how you solved your addition story.

9 **Part A**

Look at the numbers you used in your addition story.
Use the same numbers to write a subtraction story.

_____

_____

Part B

Write an equation to show your subtraction story.
Make a Proof Drawing of your subtraction story.

____ − ____ = ____

Tell how you solved your subtraction story.

Dear Family:

Your child has started a new unit on story problems. Because most children this age are learning to read, your child may need help reading the story problems. Offer help when it is needed, but do not give the answer.

To solve story problems, children first need to know which number is unknown. Is it the total or one of the parts? This program helps children focus on this important issue by using "Math Mountains." In a Math Mountain, the total sits at the top and the parts (or partners) sit at the bottom of the mountain. Children can quickly see the relationship between the partners and the total when they look at the mountain.

$$6$$
$$4 + 2$$

Math Mountain

Math Mountains are especially helpful in showing children how to find an unknown partner, as in the following problem: *I see 9 horses. 5 are black, and the others are white. How many horses are white?*

Children can find the answer by drawing the mountain to see which number is unknown. Then they count on from the partner they know to the total. In this way, they can find the partner they don't know.

Math Mountain with Unknown Partner

$$9$$
$$5 + \boxed{}$$

$$6\ 7\ 8\ 9$$
$$5$$
4 more to 9

$$9$$
$$5 + 4$$

If you have any questions, please contact me.

Sincerely,
Your child's teacher

Estimada familia:

Su niño ha empezado una nueva unidad donde aprenderá cómo resolver problemas matemáticos. Como la mayoría de los niños a esta edad aún están aprendiendo a leer, es probable que su niño necesite ayuda para leer los problemas. Ofrezca ayuda cuando haga falta, pero no dé la respuesta.

Para resolver problemas, los niños primero deben hallar el número desconocido. ¿Es el total o una de las partes? Este programa los ayuda a concentrarse en este punto importante usando "Montañas matemáticas". En una montaña matemática el total está en la cima y las partes están al pie de la montaña. Al ver la montaña, los niños pueden ver rápidamente la relación entre las partes y el total.

Montaña matemática

Las montañas matemáticas son especialmente útiles para mostrar a los niños cómo hallar una parte desconocida, como en el problema siguiente: *Veo 9 caballos. 5 son negros y los demás son blancos. ¿Cuántos caballos son blancos?*

Los niños pueden hallar la respuesta dibujando la montaña para saber cuál es el número desconocido. Luego, cuentan hacia adelante a partir de la parte que conocen para hallar el total. De esta manera, pueden hallar la parte desconocida.

Montaña matemática con parte desconocida

4 más hasta 9

Si tiene alguna pregunta, por favor comuníquese conmigo.

Atentamente,
El maestro de su niño

Explore Unknowns

subtraction
story problem

© Houghton Mifflin Harcourt Publishing Company

8 flies are on a log.
6 are eaten by a frog.
How many flies are left?

$3 + \boxed{} = 6$

$3 + \boxed{} = 7$

$3 + \boxed{} = 8$

$3 + \boxed{} = 9$

$3 + \boxed{} = 10$

$4 + \boxed{} = 7$

$4 + \boxed{} = 8$

$4 + \boxed{} = 9$

$4 + \boxed{} = 10$

$5 + \boxed{} = 8$

$5 + \boxed{} = 9$

$5 + \boxed{} = 10$

$6 + \boxed{} = 9$

$6 + \boxed{} = 10$

$7 + \boxed{} = 10$

$3 + \boxed{5} = 8$

$3 | \bullet\bullet\bullet\bullet\bullet$

$3 + \boxed{4} = 7$

$3 | \bullet\bullet\bullet\bullet$

$3 + \boxed{3} = 6$

$3 | \bullet\bullet\bullet$

$4 + \boxed{3} = 7$

$4 | \bullet\bullet\bullet$

$3 + \boxed{7} = 10$

$3 | \bullet\bullet\bullet\bullet\bullet\bullet\bullet$

$3 + \boxed{6} = 9$

$3 | \bullet\bullet\bullet\bullet\bullet\bullet$

$4 + \boxed{6} = 10$

$4 | \bullet\bullet\bullet\bullet\bullet\bullet$

$4 + \boxed{5} = 9$

$4 | \bullet\bullet\bullet\bullet\bullet$

$4 + \boxed{4} = 8$

$4 | \bullet\bullet\bullet\bullet$

$5 + \boxed{5} = 10$

$5 | \bullet\bullet\bullet\bullet\bullet$

$5 + \boxed{4} = 9$

$5 | \bullet\bullet\bullet\bullet$

$5 + \boxed{3} = 8$

$5 | \bullet\bullet\bullet$

$7 + \boxed{3} = 10$

$7 | \bullet\bullet\bullet$

$6 + \boxed{4} = 10$

$6 | \bullet\bullet\bullet\bullet$

$6 + \boxed{3} = 9$

$6 | \bullet\bullet\bullet$

Yellow Count-On Cards

Number Quilt 2: Unknown Partners

Use with the Yellow or Orange Count-On Cards.

Count on to find the unknown partner.

1 2 + ☐ = 5   **2** 4 + ☐ = 7   **3** 5 + ☐ = 9

Count on to solve.

4 7 pencils total

How many pencils are in the box?

☐ _____
        label

5 10 pennies total

How many pennies are in the box?

☐ _____
        label

Name _____ Date _____

Add.

1. $1 + 1 = $ ☐

2. $2 + 8 = $ ☐

3. $8 + 2 = $ ☐

4. $3 + 7 = $ ☐

5. $2 + 2 = $ ☐

6. $1 + 9 = $ ☐

7. $0 + 10 = $ ☐

8. $4 + 6 = $ ☐

9. $3 + 3 = $ ☐

10. $9 + 1 = $ ☐

11. $4 + 4 = $ ☐

12. $6 + 4 = $ ☐

13. $5 + 5 = $ ☐

14. $10 + 0 = $ ☐

15. $7 + 3 = $ ☐

$6 - 3 = \boxed{}$

$7 - 3 = \boxed{}$

$8 - 3 = \boxed{}$

$9 - 3 = \boxed{}$

$10 - 3 = \boxed{}$

$7 - 4 = \boxed{}$

$8 - 4 = \boxed{}$

$9 - 4 = \boxed{}$

$10 - 4 = \boxed{}$

$8 - 5 = \boxed{}$

$9 - 5 = \boxed{}$

$10 - 5 = \boxed{}$

$9 - 6 = \boxed{}$

$10 - 6 = \boxed{}$

$10 - 7 = \boxed{}$

$8 - 3 = \boxed{5}$

| 3 | ••••• |

$7 - 3 = \boxed{4}$

| 3 | •••• |

$6 - 3 = \boxed{3}$

| 3 | ••• |

$7 - 4 = \boxed{3}$

| 4 | ••• |

$10 - 3 = \boxed{7}$

| 3 | ••• ••• • |

$9 - 3 = \boxed{6}$

| 3 | • ••••• |

$10 - 4 = \boxed{6}$

| 4 | • ••••• |

$9 - 4 = \boxed{5}$

| 4 | ••••• |

$8 - 4 = \boxed{4}$

| 4 | •••• |

$10 - 5 = \boxed{5}$

| 5 | ••••• |

$9 - 5 = \boxed{4}$

| 5 | •••• |

$8 - 5 = \boxed{3}$

| 5 | ••• |

$10 - 7 = \boxed{3}$

| 7 | ••• |

$10 - 6 = \boxed{4}$

| 6 | •••• |

$9 - 6 = \boxed{3}$

| 6 | ••• |

Orange Count-On Cards

Number Quilt 3: Any Unknown

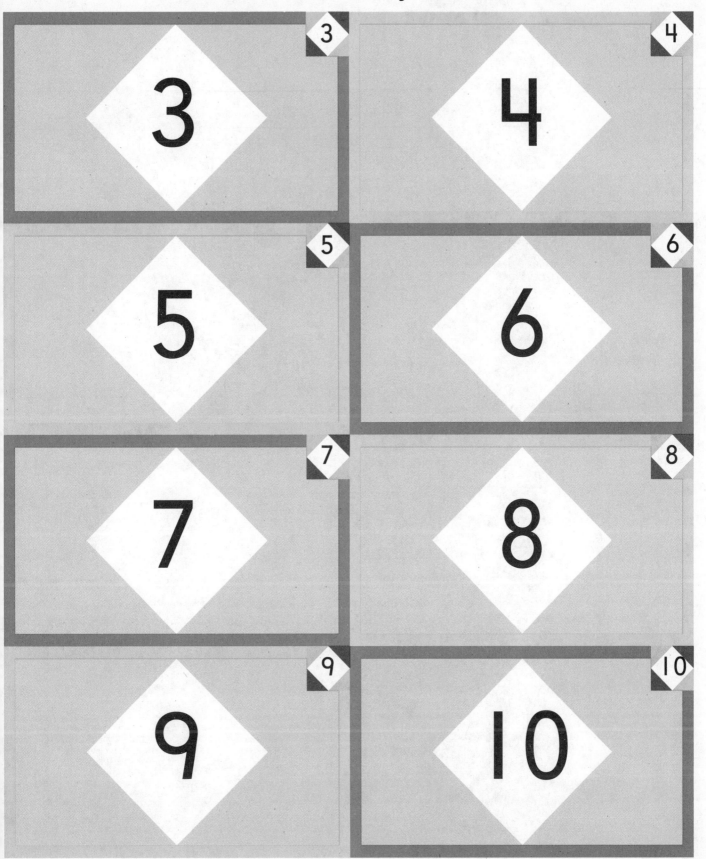

Use with any of the Count-On Cards.

Name _____

Date _____

Find the unknown partner or total.
Watch the signs.

1 $6 - 5 = \boxed{}$

2 $8 + 2 = \boxed{}$

3 $7 - \boxed{} = 1$

Solve the story problem.   **Show your work.**

4 Kyle catches 8 frogs.
He lets some frogs go.
Now Kyle has 2 frogs.
How many frogs did he let go?

$\boxed{}$ _____
label

---

5 Some birds are in a tree. Then 4 birds fly away.
Now there are 5 birds. How many birds
are in the tree at the start?

$\boxed{}$ _____
label

Name _____ Date _____

Subtract.

1 2 – 1 = ☐   **2** 3 – 3 = ☐   **3** 1 – 1 = ☐

4 2 – 2 = ☐   **5** 4 – 2 = ☐   **6** 5 – 5 = ☐

7 7 – 7 = ☐   **8** 6 – 6 = ☐   **9** 6 – 3 = ☐

10 8 – 8 = ☐   **11** 8 – 4 = ☐   **12** 9 – 9 = ☐

13 10 – 10 = ☐ **14** 10 – 5 = ☐ **15** 4 – 4 = ☐

1 Match each set of partners to a total.

6 + 2 = _____ •   • 5

9 − 3 = _____ •   • 10

3 + 7 = _____ •   • 8

8 − 3 = _____ •   • 6

Make three different Math Mountains with a total of 6.

2

☐ + ☐

3

☐ + ☐

4

☐ + ☐

5 Count on to solve.

8 rakes total

How many rakes are in the shed?

_____
label

Solve the story problem.

6 Maisy has 5 balloons. She gets some more balloons. Now she has 9 balloons. How many balloons does Maisy get?

balloon

[ ] _____
      label

---

7 Han picks 5 apples.
Then he picks 3 more.
How many apples does Han pick?

apple

[ ] _____
      label

---

8 Avery has 7 baseballs. Then he gets some more. Now Avery has 10 baseballs. How many baseballs does he get?

ball

[ ] _____
      label

Complete the equations.
Use the numbers on the tiles.

 6   5   4   8

9 $10 - [\ ] = 2$

10 $4 + [\ ] = 8$

11 $3 + [\ ] = 9$

12 $8 - [\ ] = 3$

Ring the number that makes the sentence true.

13 Lila has 10 books. She gives 4 books away.

book

Now Lila has [4 / 6 / 10] books.

14 Use the picture to write a story problem.
Write and solve the equation.

_____

_ _

_____

_ _

_____

_ _

_____

label

Solve the story problem.

15 Marty sees 8 birds at a feeder.
There are red birds and blue birds.
How many of each color bird can Marty see?
Show three correct answers.

bird

[ ] red birds and [ ] blue birds

or [ ] red birds and [ ] blue birds

or [ ] red birds and [ ] blue birds

16 Read the story problem. Write a subtraction
and an addition equation for the story.
Draw a Math Mountain to match.

There are 7 leaves on the branch.
Then 3 leaves fall off.
How many leaves are on the branch now?

Hide and Seek

Some children are playing hide and seek.

Choose a number from 1–10 for each ☐ .
Use each number only once.

1 10 children are playing. ☐ go and hide.
How many are left?

☐ children

2 ☐ children are hiding. ☐ more children
hide. How many children are hiding?

☐ children

3 Write equations for Problems 1 and 2.

☐ ◯ ☐ = ☐ | ☐ ◯ ☐ = ☐

4 Show you know which partners and total to write in
each equation. Use drawings, numbers, or words.

Soccer

Some children are playing soccer.
Choose a number from 1–10. Use each number only once.

5 **Part A** 10 children play soccer. ☐ players leave.

How many are left? ☐ children

Part B Draw a picture to tell the story.

Write an equation for the story. ☐ ◯ ☐ = ☐

6 **Part A** 4 children play soccer. ☐ players join.

How many in all? ☐ children

Part B Draw a picture to tell the story.

Write an equation for the story. ☐ ◯ ☐ = ☐

Dear Family:

Your child is learning about place value and numbers to 100. In this program, children begin by counting tens: 10, 20, 30, 40, and so on. They use a 10 × 10 Grid to help them "see" the relationship between the tens digit in a decade number and the number of tens it has.

10 20 30 40

40 is 4 tens.

Soon, children will link 2-digit numbers to tens and extra ones. They will learn that a 2-digit number, such as 46, is made up of tens and ones, such as 40 and 6. Next, children will use what they know about adding 1-digit numbers to add 2-digit numbers.

$$3 + 4 = 7, \text{ so } 30 + 40 = 70.$$

Finally, they will learn to regroup and count on to find a total. For example:

$$19 + 5 = \boxed{24}$$

⃝19⃝ 20 ∘∘∘∘ 24

Right now, your child may enjoy counting by tens for you. He or she may also enjoy using household items to make groups of ten and extra ones, and then telling you the total number.

Sincerely,
Your child's teacher

Estimada familia:

Su niño está aprendiendo sobre valor posicional y los números hasta 100. En este programa, los niños empiezan contando decenas: 10, 20, 30, 40, etc. Usan una cuadrícula de 10 por 10 como ayuda para "ver" la relación entre el dígito de las decenas en el número que termina en cero y el número de decenas que tiene.

10 20 30 40

40 es 4 decenas.

En poco tiempo, los niños harán la conexión entre números de 2 dígitos y decenas más otras unidades. Aprenderán que un número de 2 dígitos, tal como 46, consta de decenas y unidades, como 40 y 6. Luego, los niños usarán lo que saben de la suma de números de 1 dígito para sumar números de 2 dígitos.

$$3 + 4 = 7, \text{ por lo tanto } 30 + 40 = 70.$$

Finalmente, aprenderán a reagrupar y contar hacia adelante para hallar el total. Por ejemplo:

$$19 + 5 = \boxed{24}$$

20
(19) ○ ○ ○ ○ ○ 24

Por lo pronto, tal vez a su niño le guste contar en decenas para Ud. También puede gustarle usar objetos del hogar para formar grupos de diez más otras unidades y luego decir el número total.

Atentamente,
El maestro de su niño

compare

doubles
minus 2

dime

doubles
plus 1

doubles
minus 1

doubles
plus 2

7 + 7 = 14, so
7 + 5 = 12, 2 less than 14.

11 is less than 12.
11 < 12
12 is greater than 11.
12 > 11

6 + 6 = 12, so
6 + 7 = 13, 1 more than 12.

front   back
10 cents or 10¢

6 + 6 = 12, so
6 + 8 = 14, 2 more than 12.

7 + 7 = 14, so
7 + 6 = 13, 1 less than 14.

number word

quarter

tens

12
twelve ←—— **number word**

front   back

25 cents or 25¢

tens

56 has 5 **tens**.

Name _____

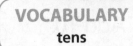
VOCABULARY
tens

How many circles? Count by **tens**.

___ ___ ___ ___ ___ ___ ___ ___

Total ____

Add 1 ten.

Equation _____

Equation _____

Equation _____

Equation _____

Add 10.

6 50 + 10 = ☐

7 10 + 10 = ☐

8 30 + 10 = ☐

9 80 + 10 = ☐

10 70 + 10 = ☐

11 60 + 10 = ☐

12 40 + 10 = ☐

13 90 + 10 = ☐

Write the numbers.

14 20 = _____ tens _____ ones

15 80 = _____ tens _____ ones

16 50 = _____ tens _____ ones

17 10 = _____ ten _____ ones

18 Draw tens to solve.
Write the unknown number.

☐ + 10 = 30

✓ **Check Understanding**
How are counting tens and
adding tens the same?

© Houghton Mifflin Harcourt Publishing Company

Introduction to Tens Groupings

Solve. Write an equation to show
one ten and extra ones.

1 Choi has 10 pencils in a pack and
4 extra pencils. How many pencils
does he have in all?

pencil

[ ] + [ ] = [ ]   [ ] pencils

2 There are 10 cups in a box and
7 extra cups. How many cups
are there altogether?

cup

[ ] + [ ] = [ ]   [ ] cups

3 Ginger has a tray of 10 plants and
2 extra plants. How many plants
are there in all?

plant

[ ] + [ ] = [ ]   [ ] plants

4 Abe has a pail of 10 brushes
and 8 extra brushes. How many
brushes are there in all?

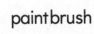

paintbrush

[ ] + [ ] = [ ]   [ ] brushes

© Houghton Mifflin Harcourt Publishing Company

Draw circles in the grid to show
the teen number. Write the equation.

5 Model 16

_____ + _____ = _____

6 Model 13

_____ + _____ = _____

7 Model 11

_____ + _____ = _____

8 There is a set of 10 books on a shelf
and 5 extra books. How many books
are there altogether?

Show the teen number in two different ways.

 Check Understanding

Explain what a teen number is.

Explore Teen Numbers

© Houghton Mifflin Harcourt Publishing Company

Dear Family:

To help children "see" the tens and ones in 2-digit numbers, the *Math Expressions* program uses special drawings of 10-sticks to show tens, and circles to show ones. These images help children learn place value. Below are the numbers 27 and 52 shown with 10-sticks and circles:

10-sticks and circles will also be used later to help children solve addition problems that require regrouping (sometimes called "carrying"). When there are enough circles to make a new ten, they are circled and then added like a 10-stick. The problem below shows 38 + 5:

Step 1: Show the two numbers with 10-sticks and circles.

Step 2: Group the ones to make a new ten. Count by tens and ones.

Right now, your child is just beginning to show teen numbers with 10-sticks and circles. Soon your child will be able to draw 10-sticks and circles for any 2-digit number.

In this unit, children will also use coins to help them understand place value, find equivalent values between coins, and solve coin story problems. As they complete their homework, they may use real or play coins to help them.

Sincerely,
Your child's teacher

Estimada familia:

Para ayudar a los niños a "ver" las decenas y las unidades en los números de 2 dígitos, el programa *Math Expressions* usa dibujos especiales de palitos de decenas para mostrar las decenas, y círculos para mostrar las unidades. Estas imágenes ayudan a los niños a aprender el valor posicional. Abajo se muestran los números 27 y 52 con palitos de decenas y círculos:

Más adelante, los palitos de decenas y los círculos también se usarán para ayudar a los niños a resolver problemas de suma que requieren reagrupar (que a veces se llama "llevar"). Cuando hay suficientes círculos para formar una nueva decena, se encierran en un círculo y se suman como si fueran un palito de decena. El siguiente problema muestra 38 + 5:

Paso 1: Mostrar los dos números con palitos de decenas y círculos.

Paso 2: Agrupar las unidades para formar una nueva decena. Contar en decenas y unidades.

Su niño está comenzando a mostrar los números de 11 a 19 con palitos de decenas y círculos. Pronto, podrá dibujar palitos de decenas y círculos para cualquier número de 2 dígitos.

En esta unidad los niños también usarán monedas que les servirán para comprender el valor posicional, hallar los valores equivalentes entre monedas y resolver problemas de monedas. Al completar su tarea, pueden usar monedas reales o de juego para ayudarlos.

Atentamente,
El maestro de su niño

Represent and Compare Teen Numbers

Name _____

Write the teen number for each model.

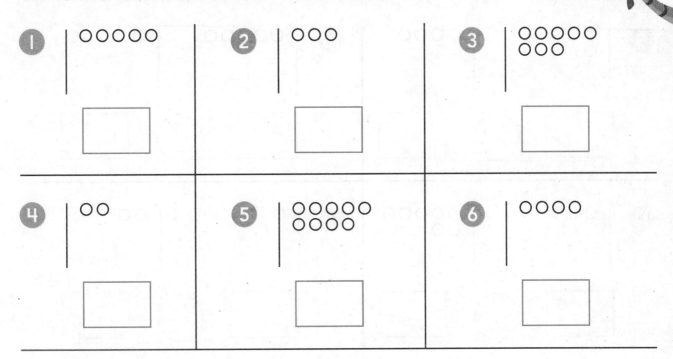

Draw a stick for 10 and circles for ones to represent the teen number.

(7) Ben buys a package of 10 erasers. He already has 2 erasers. How many erasers does Ben have now?

(8) Olivia has 16 bottles of water. A box holds 10. Draw a stick and circles to show how many boxes she can fill and how many bottles will be left over.

Write the number. Compare the numbers. Use =, <, or >.

9 | ○○○○○ ○ | ○○○○

☐ ◯ ☐

10 | ○○○○○ | ○○○○○

☐ ◯ ☐

11 | ○○○ | ○○○○○ ○○

☐ ◯ ☐

12 | ○ | ○○

☐ ◯ ☐

13 | ○○○○○ ○○○○ | ○○○○○ ○○○

☐ ◯ ☐

14 |

☐ ◯ ☐

15 Compare the numbers 16 and 12 two
different ways. Draw to explain.

✓ Check Understanding
Draw to explain why 15 is greater than 11.

Represent and Compare Teen Numbers

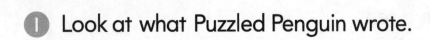

1   Look at what Puzzled Penguin wrote.

$$7 + 8 = 10 + \boxed{3}$$

$$7 + 8 = \boxed{13}$$

Am I correct?

2   Help Puzzled Penguin.

$$7 + 8 = 10 + \boxed{}$$

$$7 + 8 = \boxed{}$$

Find the total. Then make a ten.

3 7 + 4 = ☐

10 + ☐ = ☐

4 8 + 8 = ☐

10 + ☐ = ☐

5 8 + 4 = ☐

10 + ☐ = ☐

6 9 + 6 = ☐

10 + ☐ = ☐

7 8 + 6 = ☐

10 + ☐ = ☐

8 5 + 7 = ☐

10 + ☐ = ☐

9 5 + 8 = ☐

10 + ☐ = ☐

10 2 + 9 = ☐

10 + ☐ = ☐

11 Write two equations that show different partners for 13. Use 10 in one equation.

_____

_____

✔ **Check Understanding**

How can 10 + 4 help you solve 9 + 5?

Visualize Teen Addition

5 + 7 = ☐

6 + 7 = ☐

9 + 9 = ☐

8 + 7 = ☐

9 + 7 = ☐

3 + 8 = ☐

4 + 8 = ☐

5 + 8 = ☐

6 + 8 = ☐

7 + 8 = ☐

8 + 8 = ☐

9 + 8 = ☐

3 + 9 = ☐

4 + 9 = ☐

5 + 9 = ☐

Green Make-a-Ten Cards

$9 + 9 = \boxed{18}$

9	•	•••••
		•••••

9 + 1 + 8

$6 + 7 = \boxed{13}$

| 7 | ••• | ••• |

7 + 3 + 3

$5 + 7 = \boxed{12}$

| 7 | ••• | •• |

7 + 3 + 2

$3 + 8 = \boxed{11}$

| 8 | •• | • |

8 + 2 + 1

$9 + 7 = \boxed{16}$

| 9 | • | ••••• |
| | | • |

9 + 1 + 6

$8 + 7 = \boxed{15}$

| 8 | •• | ••••• |

8 + 2 + 5

$6 + 8 = \boxed{14}$

| 8 | •• | •••• |

8 + 2 + 4

$5 + 8 = \boxed{13}$

| 8 | •• | ••• |

8 + 2 + 3

$4 + 8 = \boxed{12}$

| 8 | •• | •• |

8 + 2 + 2

$9 + 8 = \boxed{17}$

| 9 | • | ••••• |
| | | •• |

9 + 1 + 7

$8 + 8 = \boxed{16}$

| 8 | •• | ••••• |
| | | • |

8 + 2 + 6

$7 + 8 = \boxed{15}$

| 8 | •• | ••••• |

8 + 2 + 5

$5 + 9 = \boxed{14}$

| 9 | • | •••• |

9 + 1 + 4

$4 + 9 = \boxed{13}$

| 9 | • | ••• |

9 + 1 + 3

$3 + 9 = \boxed{12}$

| 9 | • | •• |

9 + 1 + 2

Green Make-a-Ten Cards

6+9 = ☐   7+9 = ☐   7+4 = ☐

8+4 = ☐   9+4 = ☐   6+5 = ☐

7+5 = ☐   8+5 = ☐   9+5 = ☐

5+6 = ☐   8+9 = ☐   7+6 = ☐

8+6 = ☐   9+6 = ☐   4+7 = ☐

$7 + 4 = \boxed{11}$

| 7 | • • •   • |

7 + 3 + 1

$7 + 9 = \boxed{16}$

| 9 | •   • • • • • |

9 + 1 + 6

$6 + 9 = \boxed{15}$

| 9 | •   • • • • • |

9 + 1 + 5

$6 + 5 = \boxed{11}$

| 6 | • • • •   • |

6 + 4 + 1

$9 + 4 = \boxed{13}$

| 9 | •   • • • |

9 + 1 + 3

$8 + 4 = \boxed{12}$

| 8 | • •   • • |

8 + 2 + 2

$9 + 5 = \boxed{14}$

| 9 | •   • • • • |

9 + 1 + 4

$8 + 5 = \boxed{13}$

| 8 | • •   • • • |

8 + 2 + 3

$7 + 5 = \boxed{12}$

| 7 | • • •   • • |

7 + 3 + 2

$7 + 6 = \boxed{13}$

| 7 | • • •   • • • |

7 + 3 + 3

$8 + 9 = \boxed{17}$

| 9 | •   • • • • • • • |

9 + 1 + 7

$5 + 6 = \boxed{11}$

| 6 | • • • •   • |

6 + 4 + 1

$4 + 7 = \boxed{11}$

| 7 | • • •   • |

7 + 3 + 1

$9 + 6 = \boxed{15}$

| 9 | •   • • • • • |

9 + 1 + 5

$8 + 6 = \boxed{14}$

| 8 | • •   • • • • |

8 + 2 + 4

Green Make-a-Ten Cards

Name _____

Find the teen total.

1. $5 + 9 = \boxed{}$

2. $7 + 5 = \boxed{}$

3. $7 + 4 = \boxed{}$

4. $9 + 6 = \boxed{}$

5. $9 + 8 = \boxed{}$

6. $9 + 9 = \boxed{}$

7. $3 + 9 = \boxed{}$

8. $7 + 8 = \boxed{}$

9. $9 + 4 = \boxed{}$

10. $6 + 5 = \boxed{}$

11. $8 + 8 = \boxed{}$

12. $8 + 4 = \boxed{}$

13. $7 + 6 = \boxed{}$

14. $9 + 7 = \boxed{}$

15. Write an equation with a teen total. Draw or explain how making a ten can help you solve your equation.

_____

Teen Addition Strategies **169**

Find the total.

16 $10 + 9 =$ ☐   17 $9 + 10 =$ ☐

18 $6 + 4 =$ ☐   19 $10 + 3 =$ ☐

20 $10 + 8 =$ ☐   21 $3 + 10 =$ ☐

22 $1 + 9 =$ ☐   23 $10 + 10 =$ ☐

24 Draw or write to explain how you solved Exercise 23.

 Check Understanding

Explain how to use the Make a Ten strategy to solve $8 + 6$?

Teen Addition Strategies

Name _____

Use doubles to find the total.

1 $5 + 5 =$ ☐ **2** $6 + 6 =$ ☐ **3** $7 + 7 =$ ☐

4 $8 + 8 =$ ☐ **5** $9 + 9 =$ ☐ **6** $10 + 10 =$ ☐

Use doubles plus 1 or doubles minus 1 to find the total.

7 $4 + 4 = 8$
$4 + 5 = 8 +$ ___ $=$ ___

8 $8 + 8 = 16$
$8 + 7 = 16 -$ ___ $=$ ___

9 $5 + 6 =$ ☐ **10** $9 + 8 =$ ☐ **11** $6 + 7 =$ ☐

Use doubles plus 2 or doubles minus 2 to find the total.

12 $4 + 4 = 8$
$4 + 6 = 8 +$ ___ $=$ ___

13 $8 + 8 = 16$
$8 + 6 = 16 -$ ___ $=$ ___

14 $7 + 5 =$ ☐ **15** $7 + 9 =$ ☐ **16** $6 + 8 =$ ☐

Investigate Doubles **171**

Use a double to find the total.

17   8
    + 7

18   10
    + 8

19   5
    + 7

20   6
    + 5

21   8
    + 9

22   7
    + 8

23   7
    + 5

24   7
    + 6

25 Write the double you used to solve Exercise 23.

_____

PATH to FLUENCY Subtract.

1   6
   − 5

2   9
   − 2

3   7
   − 3

4   8
   − 2

5   10
   − 1

6   9
   − 4

7   8
   − 5

8   10
   − 8

 Check Understanding

Write a doubles plus 1 equation for 6 + 6.

_____

Investigate Doubles

Find the total. Then make a ten.

1 $7 + 5 = \boxed{}$

$10 + \boxed{} = \boxed{}$

2 $2 + 9 = \boxed{}$

$10 + \boxed{} = \boxed{}$

Use doubles or doubles plus 1 to find the total.

3 $6 + 6 = \boxed{}$

4 $9 + 8 = \boxed{}$

5 $8 + 7 = \boxed{}$

Name _____   Date _____

PATH to
FLUENCY

Subtract.

1   6
    − 2
    ‾‾‾

2   8
    − 1
    ‾‾‾

3   7
    − 0
    ‾‾‾

4   8
    − 4
    ‾‾‾

5   7
    − 3
    ‾‾‾

6   6
    − 3
    ‾‾‾

7   9
    − 4
    ‾‾‾

8   6
    − 5
    ‾‾‾

9   7
    − 2
    ‾‾‾

10   10
    − 5
    ‾‾‾

11   9
    − 6
    ‾‾‾

12   10
    − 2
    ‾‾‾

13   9
    − 7
    ‾‾‾

14   10
    − 9
    ‾‾‾

15   8
    − 5
    ‾‾‾

Name _____

Write the number.

(1) ‖ ○○○

☐

(2) ‖‖‖‖ ○○○○○ ○○

☐

(3) ‖‖‖‖‖ ○

☐

(4) ‖‖‖ ○○○○○ ○○○○

☐

(5) ‖‖‖‖ ○○○○○

☐

(6) ‖‖‖‖‖ ○○○

☐

(7) ‖ ○○

☐

(8) ‖‖‖‖ ○○○○

☐

(9) ‖‖‖‖‖ ○○

☐

(10) ‖‖‖ ○○○○○ ○○○

☐

(11) ‖‖‖‖‖ ○

☐

(12) ‖‖‖‖‖‖‖‖

☐

© Houghton Mifflin Harcourt Publishing Company

Draw 10-sticks and circles. Write the equation.

13   32

▭ + ▭ = ▭

14   68

▭ + ▭ = ▭

15   93

▭ + ▭ = ▭

16   77

▭ + ▭ = ▭

Draw 10-sticks and circles. Write the number.

17   4 tens 8 ones

▭

18   8 tens 3 ones

▭

 Check Understanding

Draw 10-sticks and circles to show 63.
Write the number of tens and ones.

     Understand Tens and Ones

Name _____

1 one	11 eleven	10 ten
2 two	12 twelve	20 twenty
3 three	13 thirteen	30 thirty
4 four	14 fourteen	40 forty
5 five	15 fifteen	50 fifty
6 six	16 sixteen	60 sixty
7 seven	17 seventeen	70 seventy
8 eight	18 eighteen	80 eighty
9 nine	19 nineteen	90 ninety
10 ten	20 twenty	

Write the number.

1 five _____   fifteen _____   fifty _____

2 three _____   thirteen _____   thirty _____

3 two _____   twelve _____   twenty _____

4 sixty _____   sixteen _____   six _____

5 eighteen _____   eighty _____   eight _____

Write the **number word**.

6 4 _____   14 _____   40 _____

7 9 _____   19 _____   90 _____

8 2 _____   12 _____   20 _____

9 1 _____   10 _____   11 _____

1 one	11 eleven	10 ten
2 two	12 twelve	20 twenty
3 three	13 thirteen	30 thirty
4 four	14 fourteen	40 forty
5 five	15 fifteen	50 fifty
6 six	16 sixteen	60 sixty
7 seven	17 seventeen	70 seventy
8 eight	18 eighteen	80 eighty
9 nine	19 nineteen	90 ninety
10 ten	20 twenty	

Write the number word.

⑩ │ ○○ _____

⑪ │ ║ _____

⑫ │║║║║║ _____

⑬ │ ○○○○○ _____

⑭ │ ○○○○○ ○○ _____

⑮ │║║║║║ ║║ _____

⑯ **Write the numbers 1–20.**

1									
									20

⑰ **Write the decade numbers 10–90.**

10	20							

Integrate Tens and Ones

Dime Strips, Dimes, and Pennies

Dime Strips, Dimes, and Pennies

Look at the **dimes** and pennies.

VOCABULARY
dime

Ring 46 cents.

Ring 83 cents.

How many cents?

© Houghton Mifflin Harcourt Publishing Company

Draw dimes and pennies to solve the equation.

23 Lucas has 7¢ in his pocket.
He has 6¢ in his hand.
How much money does
Lucas have?

$7¢ + 6¢ = $ ⬚ ¢

---

24 Alma has 8¢ in her bank.
Her mom gives her 8¢.
How much money does
Alma have?

$8¢ + 8¢ = $ ⬚ ¢

---

25 Fiona finds 9¢ in her coat.
She finds 6¢ on her desk.
How much money does
Fiona find?

$9¢ + 6¢ = $ ⬚ ¢

✓ **Check Understanding**
Explain how the numbers 2, 12, and 20 are
the same and how they are different.

Integrate Tens and Ones

Name _____

Draw 10-sticks and circles.
Write the total.

1 [ ] = 50 + 3

2 [ ] = 70 + 6

3 [ ] = 20 + 9

4 [ ] = 40 + 2

5 [ ] = 30 + 7

6 [ ] = 10 + 8

7 [ ] = 90 + 1

8 [ ] = 50 + 5

Practice Grouping Ones into Tens **183**

Draw 10-sticks and circles to add.
Write the total.

9

24 + 3 = ☐

10 ‖ ○○○○○
      ○○

27 + 6 = ☐

11

41 + 5 = ☐

12 ‖‖‖‖‖ ○○○○○
             ○○○○

79 + 5 = ☐

13

67 + 2 = ☐

14 ‖‖‖‖ ○○○○

54 + 4 = ☐

15

65 + 6 = ☐

16 ‖‖‖ ○○○

33 + 7 = ☐

✓ **Check Understanding**
Explain how to add 29 + 3.

Practice Grouping Ones into Tens

Name _____

Each box has 10 muffins. How many muffins are there?

1

2

3

4

5

6 How are 23 and 32 the same?
How are they different?

PATH to FLUENCY Add.

1. $3 + 3 = \boxed{}$ 2. $4 + 5 = \boxed{}$ 3. $1 + 5 = \boxed{}$

4. $3 + 7 = \boxed{}$ 5. $8 + 0 = \boxed{}$ 6. $2 + 5 = \boxed{}$

7. $\boxed{} = 5 + 2$ 8. $\boxed{} = 7 + 1$ 9. $\boxed{} = 5 + 5$

10. $\boxed{} = 1 + 6$ 11. $\boxed{} = 7 + 3$ 12. $\boxed{} = 5 + 3$

PATH to FLUENCY Find the unknown number.

13. $2 + \boxed{} = 9$ 14. $6 + \boxed{} = 10$ 15. $4 + \boxed{} = 7$

16. $8 + \boxed{} = 10$ 17. $3 + \boxed{} = 8$ 18. $1 + \boxed{} = 10$

19. $\boxed{} + 3 = 9$ 20. $\boxed{} + 6 = 8$ 21. $\boxed{} + 8 = 9$

22. $\boxed{} + 6 = 6$ 23. $\boxed{} + 4 = 7$ 24. $\boxed{} + 2 = 9$

✓ **Check Understanding**

Explain how to use tens and ones to find $43 + 6$.

Add with Groups of Ten

1	2	10	20
1	2	1 0	2 0

3	4	30	40
3	4	3 0	4 0

5	6	50	60
5	6	5 0	6 0

7	8	70	80
7	8	7 0	8 0

9	90	100
9	9 0	1 0 0

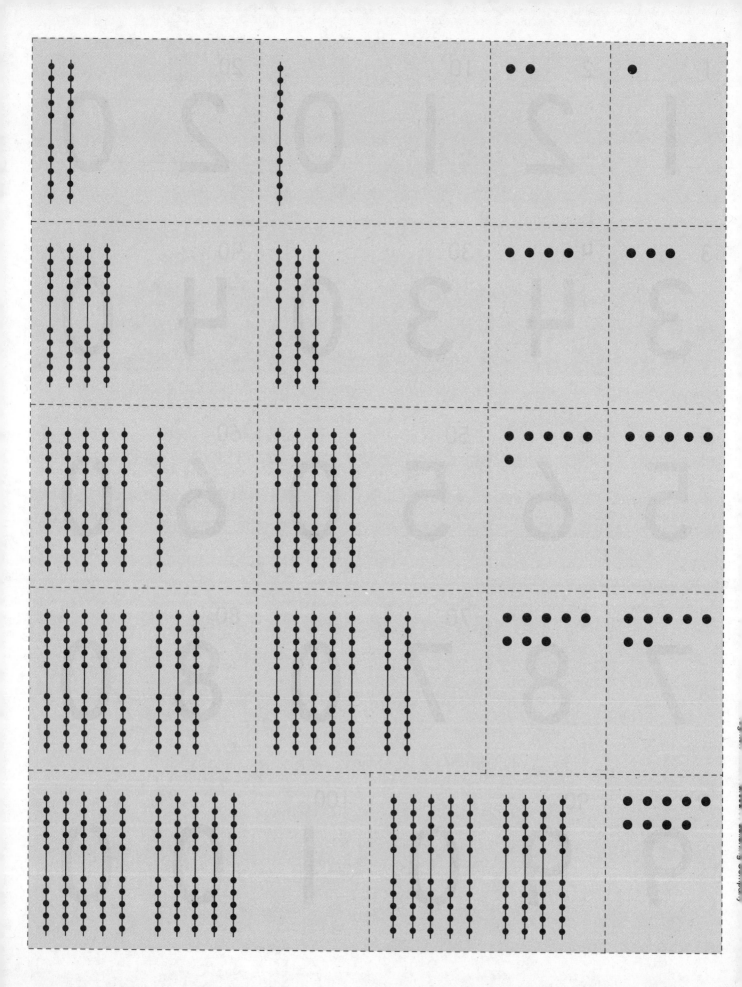

Secret Code Cards

Name _____

Write the number of tens and ones.
Write the number.

1
___ tens ___ ones

2
___ tens ___ ones

3
___ tens ___ ones

4
___ tens ___ ones

5
___ tens ___ ones

6
___ tens ___ ones

7
___ tens ___ ones

8
___ tens ___ ones

Draw 10-sticks and circles.
Write the number of tens and ones.

9   75

___ tens ___ ones

10   90

___ tens ___ ones

11   41

___ tens ___ ones

12   59

___ tens ___ ones

13   26

___ tens ___ ones

14   88

___ tens ___ ones

✓ **Check Understanding**

Draw 10-sticks and circles for a 2-digit
number that has 7 tens and another
2-digit number that has 7 ones.

Practice with Tens and Ones

Name _____

Compare the numbers. Write >, <, or =.

1

30 ◯ 25

2

23 ◯ 28

3 70 ◯ 80   **4** 60 ◯ 59   **5** 76 ◯ 67

6 24 ◯ 84   **7** 37 ◯ 37   **8** 48 ◯ 50

9 56 ◯ 56   **10** 17 ◯ 42   **11** 99 ◯ 33

Compare the numbers two ways.
Write the numbers.

12 Compare 53 and 54.

____ ◯ ____

____ ◯ ____

13 Compare 80 and 79.

____ ◯ ____

____ ◯ ____

14 Compare 49 and 94.

____ ◯ ____

____ ◯ ____

15 Compare 36 and 32.

____ ◯ ____

____ ◯ ____

Use Place Value to Compare Numbers **191**

Write to compare the numbers.

16 Compare 39 and 40.

_____ ◯ _____

17 Compare 86 and 68.

_____ ◯ _____

18 Compare 95 and 91.

_____ ◯ _____

19 Compare 72 and 72.

_____ ◯ _____

20 Compare 20 and 10.

_____ ◯ _____

21 Compare 60 and 16.

_____ ◯ _____

22 Look at what Puzzled Penguin wrote.

29 (>) 36

Am I correct?

23 Help Puzzled Penguin.

29 ◯ 36

✔ **Check Understanding**
Compare 26 and 62.

_____ ◯ _____

Use Place Value to Compare Numbers

Write the numbers.

 ① _____ tens _____ ones = _____

 ② _____ tens _____ ones = _____

Compare the numbers. Write >, <, or =.

 ③ 63 ◯ 73

 ④ 42 ◯ 24

 ⑤ 20 ◯ 20

Name _____   Date _____

PATH to FLUENCY

Find the unknown partner or total.

1 3 + 3 = ☐   **2** 2 + 4 = ☐   **3** 5 + 3 = ☐

4 3 + 4 = ☐   **5** 8 + 1 = ☐   **6** 2 + 5 = ☐

7 4 + ☐ = 6   **8** 7 + ☐ = 9   **9** 1 + ☐ = 7

10 4 + ☐ = 8   **11** 8 + ☐ = 10

12 3 + ☐ = 10   **13** ☐ + 3 = 9

14 ☐ + 5 = 8   **15** ☐ + 4 = 10

© Houghton Mifflin Harcourt Publishing Company

Name _____

Write the totals.

1 $4 + 4 =$ ▢

$40 + 40 =$ ▢

2 $6 + 3 =$ ▢

$60 + 30 =$ ▢

3 $2 + 3 =$ ▢

$20 + 30 =$ ▢

4 $1 + 7 =$ ▢

$10 + 70 =$ ▢

5 $5 + 2 =$ ▢

$50 + 20 =$ ▢

6 $3 + 3 =$ ▢

$30 + 30 =$ ▢

7 $7 + 2 =$ ▢

$70 + 20 =$ ▢

8 $2 + 2 =$ ▢

$20 + 20 =$ ▢

9 Use 10-sticks and circles to solve.

$4 + 5 =$ ▢ $40 + 50 =$ ▢

Explain how the totals are different.

_____

_____

_____

_____

Add Tens or Ones **195**

Complete the equation.
Draw a 10-stick or a circle to solve for the total.

10 14

| ○○○○

[ ] + 1 = [ ]

11 16

| ○○○○○
  ○

[ ] + 10 = [ ]

12 13

| ○○○

[ ] + 1 = [ ]

13 23

| | ○○○

[ ] + 1 = [ ]

14 39

| | | ○○○○○
    ○○○○

[ ] + 10 = [ ]

15 42

| | | | ○○

[ ] + 10 = [ ]

16 57

| | | | | ○○○○○
          ○○

[ ] + 1 = [ ]

 Check Understanding
Explain if the total of
58 + 10 will be 59 or 68.

Add Tens or Ones

Solve.

1. 3 + 6 = _____
   30 + 60 = _____
   30 + 6 = _____

2. 4 + 5 = _____
   40 + 50 = _____
   40 + 5 = _____

3. 2 + 4 = _____
   20 + 40 = _____
   20 + 4 = _____

4. 5 + 2 = _____
   50 + 20 = _____
   50 + 2 = _____

5. 7 + 2 = _____
   70 + 20 = _____
   70 + 2 = _____

6. 4 + 1 = _____
   40 + 10 = _____
   40 + 1 = _____

7. 3 + 2 = _____
   30 + 20 = _____
   30 + 2 = _____

8. 1 + 8 = _____
   10 + 80 = _____
   10 + 8 = _____

Complete the set of equations to follow the same rules as each set above. Then solve.

9. 3 + 5 = _____
   30 + _____ = _____
   30 + _____ = _____

10. 4 + 3 = _____
    40 + _____ = _____
    40 + _____ = _____

Find the unknown numbers to complete
the set of equations.

⓫ 2 + _____ = 5

20 + 30 = _____

20 + _____ = 23

⓬ 4 + _____ = 8

_____ + 40 = 80

40 + 4 = _____

⓭ _____ + 2 = 6

40 + _____ = 60

_____ + 2 = 42

⓮ _____ + 7 = 8

10 + _____ = 80

10 + 7 = _____

⓯ Look at what Puzzled Penguin wrote.

50 + 4 = $\boxed{90}$

Am I correct?

⓰ Help Puzzled Penguin.

50 + 4 = $\boxed{}$

 Check Understanding

Write tens, ones, or both to add the numbers.

40 + 30   adding _____   40 + 3   adding _____

© Houghton Mifflin Harcourt Publishing Company

Mixed Addition with Tens and Ones

Name _____

Here is a riddle.

> I like to hop,
> but my ears are small.
> I have four legs, but I stand tall.
> I have a pocket,
> but I cannot buy.
> Guess my name. Who am I?

Find the total. Use any method.

1 $46 + 5 =$ ☐ O   **2** $40 + 2 =$ ☐ O

3 $12 + 7 =$ ☐ K   **4** $29 + 5 =$ ☐ R

5 $64 + 6 =$ ☐ A   **6** $20 + 9 =$ ☐ A

7 $27 + 5 =$ ☐ G   **8** $89 + 2 =$ ☐ N

Who am I? Write the letter for each total.

___ ___ ___ ___ ___ ___ ___ ___
19   70   91   32   29   34   42   51

PATH to FLUENCY Add.

① $4 + 5 = \boxed{}$ ② $0 + 7 = \boxed{}$ ③ $7 + 3 = \boxed{}$

④ $1 + 6 = \boxed{}$ ⑤ $6 + 2 = \boxed{}$ ⑥ $4 + 2 = \boxed{}$

⑦ $\boxed{} = 7 + 1$ ⑧ $\boxed{} = 3 + 6$ ⑨ $\boxed{} = 7 + 2$

⑩ $\boxed{} = 6 + 4$ ⑪ $\boxed{} = 2 + 4$ ⑫ $\boxed{} = 4 + 3$

PATH to FLUENCY Find the unknown number.

⑬ $1 + \boxed{} = 8$ ⑭ $3 + \boxed{} = 7$ ⑮ $5 + \boxed{} = 8$

⑯ $8 + \boxed{} = 10$ ⑰ $4 + \boxed{} = 8$ ⑱ $9 + \boxed{} = 9$

⑲ $\boxed{} + 1 = 6$ ⑳ $\boxed{} + 4 = 9$ ㉑ $\boxed{} + 7 = 10$

㉒ $\boxed{} + 8 = 9$ ㉓ $\boxed{} + 5 = 8$ ㉔ $\boxed{} + 8 = 10$

✔ **Check Understanding**

Explain how to count on to find $28 + 3$.

Counting On Strategy: 2-Digit Numbers

Name _____

Use this sandwich sheet when you play
The Sandwich Game.

1

2

3

4

5

6

7

8

9

10

Practice with 2-Digit Numbers **201**

Find the total. Use any method.

⑪ 29 + 3 = ☐   ⑫ 11 + 8 = ☐

⑬ 67 + 4 = ☐   ⑭ 33 + 9 = ☐

⑮ 96 + 3 = ☐   ⑯ 46 + 4 = ☐

⑰ 12 + 8 = ☐   ⑱ 71 + 5 = ☐

Compare. Write >, <, or =.

⑲ 26 ◯ 62   ⑳ 80 ◯ 79

㉑ 18 ◯ 38   ㉒ 65 ◯ 65

㉓ 97 ◯ 94   ㉔ 45 ◯ 53

 Check Understanding

Compare 61 and 57.
Write the number that is greater. _____

Practice with 2-Digit Numbers

Write the number.

Draw 10-sticks and circles to show the number.

5

6

7

8

Draw 10-sticks and circles to count on.
Write the total.

9 Count on 4.

○○○○○
○○○

10 Count on 3.

| ○

11 Count on 6.

| ○○○○○
○○○○

12 Count on 2.

||| ○○○○○
○○○

13 Count on 5.

||||| ○○○○○
○○○○

14 Count on 4.

|||||| || ○○○○○
○

15 Count on 6.

|||||| | ○○○○○

16 Count on 4.

|||||| ||| ○○○○

 Check Understanding
Write the total for 38 + 4.

2-Digit Addition Games

Linda and her family go to a show.

1 10 cars can park in each row.

How many cars are there?

_____ tens _____ ones = _____ cars

2 10 people can sit in each row.

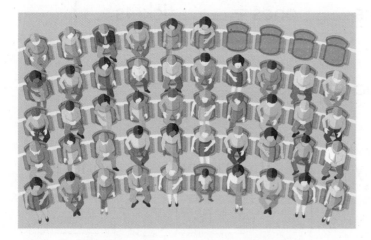

How many people are there?

_____ tens _____ ones = _____ people

Show tickets were sold on Friday,
Saturday, and Sunday.

3 Write the number of tickets sold each day.

Friday	10 TICKETS / ADMIT ONE (6 bundles of 10, 5 ADMIT ONE)
	_____ tens _____ ones = _____ tickets
Saturday	10 TICKETS / ADMIT ONE (5 bundles of 10, 4 ADMIT ONE)
	_____ tens _____ ones = _____ tickets
Sunday	10 TICKETS / ADMIT ONE (5 bundles of 10, 10 ADMIT ONE)
	_____ tens _____ ones = _____ tickets

Compare the number of tickets sold.
Use >, <, or =.

4 Friday   Saturday   **5** Friday   Sunday

6 Saturday   Sunday   **7** Sunday   Saturday

     Focus on Problem Solving

Add.

1 20 + 50 = ☐

2 60 + 3 = ☐

Find the total.

3 44 + 3 = ☐

4 72 + 9 = ☐

Solve the story problem.

Show your work.

5 Cindy has 56 stamps.
She buys 4 more stamps.
How many stamps does she have now?

_____
label

Name

Date

PATH to
FLUENCY

Find the unknown partner or total.

1 $5 + 2 =$ ☐   **2** $1 + 5 =$ ☐   **3** $2 + 4 =$ ☐

4 $5 + 4 =$ ☐   **5** $2 + 6 =$ ☐   **6** $5 + 5 =$ ☐

7 $1 +$ ☐ $= 7$ **8** $4 +$ ☐ $= 6$ **9** $0 +$ ☐ $= 8$

10 $6 +$ ☐ $= 9$ **11** $2 +$ ☐ $= 8$

12 $9 +$ ☐ $= 10$ **13** ☐ $+ 3 = 6$

14 ☐ $+ 0 = 9$ **15** ☐ $+ 7 = 8$

Cut on the dotted lines.

Coins **209**

Coins

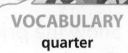

Match the dime, nickel, and **quarter** to the same amount in pennies.
Write the amount in cents.

1   •   • 5 pennies [   ] ¢

2   •   • 25 pennies [   ] ¢

3   •   • 10 pennies [   ] ¢

Draw coins to show 10¢.

4 Use pennies.

_____

5 Use nickels.

_____

6 Use dimes.

_____

7 Use nickels and pennies.

Show the price with sticks and circles.
Then write how many of each coin.

17¢   Dimes _____   Pennies _____

62¢   Dimes _____   Pennies _____

44¢   Dimes _____   Pennies _____

✓ Check Understanding

Write how many cents each coin is worth.

 _____   _____   _____

Pennies, Nickels, Dimes, and Quarters

Name _____

Ring the correct coin.

1 I am worth the same as
two nickels.
What am I?

2 You need 10 of me to
make a dime.
What am I?

3 I am worth the same as
two dimes and one nickel.
What am I?

Solve the story problems.
Write the amount using ¢.

Show your work. Use drawings, numbers, or words.

4 Jana has 1 dime, 2 nickels,
and 3 pennies. How many
cents does Jana have?

_____

5 Brooke has 2 dimes, 3 nickels,
and 2 pennies. How many
cents does Brooke have?

_____

Solve the story problems.
Write the amount using ¢.

Show your work. Use drawings, numbers, or words.

6 José bought an apple for 2 dimes, 1 nickel, and 2 pennies. How many cents did he pay?

_____

7 Lexi bought a pencil for 3 dimes, 1 nickel, and 4 pennies. How many cents did she pay?

_____

8 Mia has 3 dimes, 3 nickels, and 3 pennies on her desk. How many cents does she have?

_____

9 Chaz has 5 dimes, 4 nickels, and 3 pennies in his pocket. How many cents does he have?

_____

✓ **Check Understanding**
Ty has 2 dimes and 3 pennies. How many cents does Ty have? _____

Coin Stories

For questions 1 and 2, draw coins to show 25¢.

1 Use dimes and pennies.

2 Use nickels.

Solve the story problems.

3 Javed buys a banana with 2 dimes,
1 nickel, and 5 pennies. How many
cents does he pay?

_____

4 Marita has 5 pennies and 2 nickels.
How many cents does Marita have?

_____

5 Sam exchanges 15 pennies for nickels
and dimes. Which coins should he
get in return?

_____

Name _____ Date _____

Find the unknown partner or total.

1 $4 + 2 = \boxed{}$ **2** $1 + 4 = \boxed{}$ **3** $2 + 3 = \boxed{}$

4 $5 + 5 = \boxed{}$ **5** $2 + 7 = \boxed{}$ **6** $4 + 5 = \boxed{}$

7 $0 + \boxed{} = 6$ **8** $3 + \boxed{} = 5$ **9** $0 + \boxed{} = 9$

10 $5 + \boxed{} = 8$ **11** $1 + \boxed{} = 7$

12 $8 + \boxed{} = 10$ **13** $\boxed{} + 4 = 8$

14 $\boxed{} + 0 = 10$ **15** $\boxed{} + 5 = 6$

Name _____   Date _____

1 Does the number match the picture?
Choose Yes or No.

    50   ○ Yes   ○ No

    31   ○ Yes   ○ No

Draw 10-sticks and circles.
Write the number of tens and ones.

2   32

☐ tens ☐ ones = 32

3   64

☐ tens ☐ ones = 64

Use the words on the tiles to name each number.

| seventy | seven | seventeen |

4 17 _____

5 70 _____

6 7 _____

7 Add 1 ten.

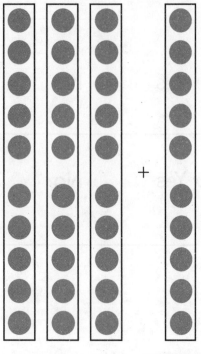

$$30 + 10 = \boxed{}$$

8 How many paper clips?

$$\boxed{}$$

9 Draw a picture for the problem.
Write an equation to solve.

There are 10 birds in one tree.
There are 7 birds in another tree.
How many birds are there?

label

$$\boxed{} + \boxed{} = \boxed{}$$

10 How many muffins are there?

○ 22
○ 25
○ 42
○ 62

11 Show 47¢ with sticks and circles.
Then write how many of each coin.

Dimes _____ Pennies _____

Solve the story problem.

12 Kimi has 8 red apples and
5 green apples. How many
apples does she have?

apple

[   ] _____
          label

13 Shonda finds 2 dimes, 3 nickels, and 3 pennies.
How many cents does she find?

[   ] _____
          label

Ring >, <, or = to compare the numbers.

⑭ 42 $\boxed{\begin{array}{c} > \\ < \\ = \end{array}}$ 50

⑮ 34 $\boxed{\begin{array}{c} > \\ < \\ = \end{array}}$ 33

Find the unknown numbers to complete
the set of equations.

⑯ 3 + _____ = 7

30 + 40 = _____

30 + _____ = 34

⑰ _____ + 7 = 9

20 + _____ = 90

20 + 7 = _____

⑱ Write a number from 10 to 40.
Add 1 ten. Write the new number.
Draw and write to compare the numbers.

Snack Time

It is snack time at sports camp. Each team gets these drinks.

Water	Milk	Orange Juice	Apple Juice
13 bottles	11 cartons	9 boxes	7 boxes

1 Does each team get more bottles of water or more

cartons of milk? _____

Draw or write to tell how you know.

2 Draw 10-sticks and circles to show the number of water bottles.

3 Each team has 20 children. Does a team get enough juice

boxes for everyone? _____

Draw or write to tell how you know.

Snack Time (continued)

Use the drink chart on page 221 for Problem 4.

4 **Part A**
The Red team has 20 children.
They choose two kinds of drinks.
Show how many they might
choose of each.

Kind of Drink	How many?

Draw or write to tell how you know there
are 20 drinks.

Part B
The Blue team has 20 children.
No children want milk.
Show how they might choose
other drinks.
(Choose at least one of each).

Kind of Drink	How many?

Draw or write to tell how you know there
are 20 drinks.

Addition and Subtraction Problem Types

	Result Unknown	Change Unknown	Start Unknown
Add To	Six children are playing tag in the yard. Three more children come to play. How many children are playing in the yard now? *Situation and Solution Equation*[1]: $6 + 3 = \square$	Six children are playing tag in the yard. Some more children come to play. Now there are 9 children in the yard. How many children came to play? *Situation Equation:* $6 + \square = 9$ *Solution Equation:* $9 - 6 = \square$	Some children are playing tag in the yard. Three more children come to play. Now there are 9 children in the yard. How many children were in the yard at first? *Situation Equation:* $\square + 3 = 9$ *Solution Equation:* $9 - 3 = \square$
Take From	Jake has 10 trading cards. He gives 3 to his brother. How many trading cards does he have left? *Situation and Solution Equation:* $10 - 3 = \square$	Jake has 10 trading cards. He gives some to his brother. Now Jake has 7 trading cards left. How many cards does he give to his brother? *Situation Equation:* $10 - \square = 7$ *Solution Equation:* $10 - 7 = \square$	Jake has some trading cards. He gives 3 to his brother. Now Jake has 7 trading cards left. How many cards does he start with? *Situation Equation:* $\square - 3 = 7$ *Solution Equation:* $7 + 3 = \square$

[1]A situation equation represents the structure (action) in the problem situation. A solution equation shows the operation used to find the answer.

Addition and Subtraction Problem Types (continued)

	Total Unknown	Addend Unknown	Other Addend Unknown
Put Together/ Take Apart	There are 9 red roses and 4 yellow roses in a vase. How many roses are in the vase? *Math Drawing²:* *Situation and Solution Equation:* $9 + 4 = \square$	Thirteen roses are in the vase. 9 are red and the rest are yellow. How many roses are yellow? *Math Drawing:* *Situation Equation:* $13 = 9 + \square$ *Solution Equation:* $13 - 9 = \square$	Thirteen roses are in the vase. Some are red and 4 are yellow. How many are red? *Math Drawing:* 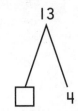 *Situation Equation:* $13 = \square + 4$ *Solution Equation:* $13 - 4 = \square$

Both Addends Unknown is a productive extension of this basic situation, especially for small numbers less than or equal to 10. Such take apart situations can be used to show all the decompositions of a given number. The associated equations, which have the total on the left of the equal sign, help children understand that the = sign does not always mean makes or results in but always does mean is the same number as.

Both Addends Unknown

Ana has 13 roses. How many can she put in her red vase and how many in her blue vase?

Math Drawing:

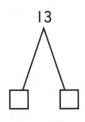

Situation Equation:
$13 = \square + \square$

²These math drawings are called Math Mountains in Grades 1–3 and break-apart drawings in Grades 4 and 5.

Addition and Subtraction Problem Types (continued)

Compare[3]	Difference Unknown	Bigger Unknown	Smaller Unknown
	Aki has 8 apples. Sofia has 14 apples. How many more apples does Sofia have than Aki? Aki has 8 apples. Sofia has 14 apples. How many fewer apples does Aki have than Sofia? *Math Drawing:* S [14] A [8] (?) *Situation Equation:* $8 + \square = 14$ *Solution Equation:* $14 - 8 = \square$	**Leading Language** Aki has 8 apples. Sofia has 6 more apples than Aki. How many apples does Sofia have? **Misleading Language** Aki has 8 apples. Aki has 6 fewer apples than Sofia. How many apples does Sofia have? *Math Drawing:* S [?] A [8] (6) *Situation and Solution Equation:* $8 + 6 = \square$	**Leading Language** Sofia has 14 apples. Aki has 6 fewer apples than Sofia. How many apples does Aki have? **Misleading Language** Sofia has 14 apples. Sofia has 6 more apples than Aki. How many apples does Aki have? *Math Drawing:* S [14] A [?] (6) *Situation Equation:* $\square + 6 = 14$ *Solution Equation:* $14 - 6 = \square$

[3]A comparison sentence can always be said in two ways. One way uses *more*, and the other uses *fewer* or *less*. Misleading language suggests the wrong operation. For example, it says *Aki has 6 fewer apples than Sofia*, but you have to add 6 to Aki's 8 apples to get 14 apples.

Glossary

5-group*

←5-group

10-group

or

10-stick*

You can show 32 with three **10-sticks** and two ones.

A

add

$$3 + 2 = 5$$

addend

$$5 + 4 = 9 \qquad 5 + 4 + 8 = 17$$

addends
(partners)   addends

addition story problem

There are 5 ducks.
Then 3 more come.
How many ducks are there now?

B

bar graph

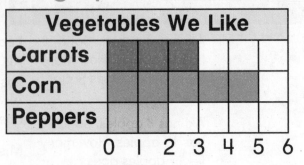

Vegetables We Like						
Carrots						
Corn						
Peppers						

0 1 2 3 4 5 6

break-apart*

You can **break apart** the number 4.

1 and 3   2 and 2   3 and 1

1 and 3, 2 and 2, and 3 and 1 are
break-aparts of 4.

C

cents (¢)

The number of cents is the value of
a coin or a set of coins.

7 cents

circle

---

*A classroom research-based term developed for *Math Expressions*

circle drawing*

clock

analog
clock

digital
clock

column

1	11	21	31	41	51	61	71	81	91
2	12	22	32	42	52	62	72	82	92
3	13	23	33	43	53	63	73	83	93
4	14	24	34	44	54	64	74	84	94
5	15	25	35	45	55	65	75	85	95
6	16	26	36	46	56	66	76	86	96
7	17	27	37	47	57	67	77	87	97
8	18	28	38	48	58	68	78	88	98
9	19	29	39	49	59	69	79	89	99
10	20	30	40	50	60	70	80	90	100

compare

You can **compare** numbers.

11 is less than 12.

$11 < 12$

12 is greater than 11.

$12 > 11$

You can **compare** objects by length.

The crayon is shorter than the pencil.
The pencil is longer than the crayon.

comparison bars*

Joe has 6 roses. Sasha has 9 roses.
How many more roses does Sasha have
than Joe?

S | 9 | comparison
J | 6 | ? | bars

cone

*A classroom research-based term developed for *Math Expressions*

corner

corner

count

1   2   3

count all

$5 + 4 = \boxed{9}$

• • • • •   • • • •

1 2 3 4 5   6 7 8 9

count on

$5 + 4 = \boxed{9}$

$5 + \boxed{4} = 9$

$9 - 5 = \boxed{4}$

5 • • • •
6 7 8 9

Count on from 5 to get the answer.

cube

cylinder

D

data

Colors in the Bag									
Red	○	○	○						
Yellow	○	○	○	○	○	○	○	○	
Blue	○	○	○	○	○	○			

The **data** show how many of each color.

decade numbers

10, 20, 30, 40, 50, 60, 70, 80, 90

*A classroom research-based term developed for *Math Expressions*

difference

$$11 - 3 = 8$$

$$\begin{array}{r} 11 \\ -3 \\ \hline \end{array}$$

difference → 8

digit

15 is a 2-**digit** number.

The 1 in 15 means 1 ten.

The 5 in 15 means 5 ones.

dime

front   back

10 cents or 10¢

dot array

doubles

$$4 + 4 = 8$$

Both partners are the same.
They are doubles.

doubles minus 1

$7 + 7 = 14$, so

$7 + 6 = 13$, 1 less than 14.

doubles minus 2

$7 + 7 = 14$, so

$7 + 5 = 12$, 2 less than 14.

doubles plus 1

$6 + 6 = 12$, so

$6 + 7 = 13$, 1 more than 12.

doubles plus 2

$6 + 6 = 12$, so

$6 + 8 = 14$, 2 more than 12.

E

edge

edge

equal shares

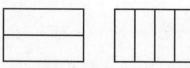

2 equal shares   4 equal shares

These show **equal shares**.

equal to (=)

$$4 + 4 = 8$$

4 plus 4 is **equal to** 8.

equation

$$4 + 3 = 7 \qquad 7 = 4 + 3$$

$$9 - 5 = 4 \qquad 4 = 9 - 5$$

F

face

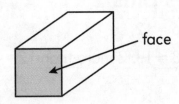

fewer

Eggs Laid This Month

Clucker laid **fewer** eggs than Vanilla.

fewest

Eggs Laid This Month

Clucker laid the **fewest** eggs.

fourth of

One **fourth of** the shape is shaded.

fourths

1 whole   4 **fourths**, or 4 quarters

G

greater than (>)

34   >   25

34 is **greater than** 25.

grid

growing pattern

1 2 3 4

H

half-hour

A **half-hour** is 30 minutes.

half of

One **half of** the shape is shaded.

halves

1 whole   2 **halves**

hexagon

hour

An **hour** is 60 minutes.

hour hand

hundred

I	II	21	31	41	51	61	71	81	91
2	12	22	32	42	52	62	72	82	92
3	13	23	33	43	53	63	73	83	93
4	14	24	34	44	54	64	74	84	94
5	15	25	35	45	55	65	75	85	95
6	16	26	36	46	56	66	76	86	96
7	17	27	37	47	57	67	77	87	97
8	18	28	38	48	58	68	78	88	98
9	19	29	39	49	59	69	79	89	99
10	20	30	40	50	60	70	80	90	100

or

K

known partner*

$5 + \boxed{} = 7$

5 is the **known partner**.

L

length

The **length** of this pencil is 6 paper clips.

---

less than (<)

45   <   46

45 is **less than** 46.

---

longer

The pencil is **longer** than the crayon.

---

longest

The pencil is the **longest**.

M

make a ten

$8 + 6 = \boxed{}$

⑧ ⓪⓪ ○○○○

$10 + 4 = 14,$
so $8 + 6 = 14.$

---

*A classroom research-based term developed for *Math Expressions*

Math Mountain*

measure

You can use paper clips to **measure** the length of the pencil.

minus (−)

$$8 - 3 = 5 \qquad \begin{array}{r} 8 \\ -3 \\ \hline 5 \end{array}$$

8 minus 3 equals 5.

minute

There are 60 **minutes** in an hour.

more

Eggs Laid This Month

Vanilla laid **more** eggs than Clucker.

most

Eggs Laid This Month

Vanilla laid the **most** eggs.

N

New Group Above Method*

$$\begin{array}{r} \overset{1}{5}6 \\ +28 \\ \hline 84 \end{array}$$

$6 + 8 = 14$

The 1 new ten in 14 goes up to the tens place.

New Group Below Method*

$$\begin{array}{r} 56 \\ +28 \\ \hline 84 \end{array}$$

$6 + 8 = 14$

The 1 new ten in 14 goes below in the tens place.

*A classroom research-based term developed for *Math Expressions*

nickel

front

back

5 cents or 5¢

not equal to (≠)

6 ≠ 8

6 is **not equal to** 8.

number line

0 1 2 3 4 5 6 7 8 9 10

number word

12

twelve ←—— number word

O

ones

ones

56 has 6 **ones**.

order

You can change the **order** of the partners.

7 + 2 = 9

2 + 7 = 9

You can **order** objects by length.

P

partner*

5 = 2 + 3

2 and 3 are **partners** of 5.
2 and 3 are 5-**partners**.

partner house*

9

5 + 4
6 + 3
3 + 6
4 + 5
7 + 2
8 + 1
2 + 7
1 + 8

*A classroom research-based term developed for *Math Expressions*

partner train*

4-train

pattern

5 = 4 + 1

5 = 3 + 2

5 = 2 + 3

5 = 1 + 4

The partners of a number show a **pattern**.

penny

front   back

1 cent or 1¢

plus (+)

$$3 + 2 = 5 \qquad \begin{array}{r} 3 \\ + 2 \\ \hline 5 \end{array}$$

3 **plus** 2 equals 5.

Proof Drawing*

Q

quarter

front   back

25 cents or 25¢

quarter of

One **quarter of** the shape is shaded.

quarters

1 whole   4 **quarters**,
                           or 4 fourths

*A classroom research-based term developed for *Math Expressions*

R

rectangle

A square is a special kind of rectangle.

rectangular prism

A cube is a special kind of rectangular prism.

repeating pattern

row

1	11	21	31	41	51	61	71	81	91
2	12	22	32	42	52	62	72	82	92
3	13	23	33	43	53	63	73	83	93
4	14	24	34	44	54	64	74	84	94
5	15	25	35	45	55	65	75	85	95
6	16	26	36	46	56	66	76	86	96
7	17	27	37	47	57	67	77	87	97
8	18	28	38	48	58	68	78	88	98
9	19	29	39	49	59	69	79	89	99
10	20	30	40	50	60	70	80	90	100

S

shapes

2-dimensional

3-dimensional

shorter

The crayon is **shorter** than the pencil.

*A classroom research-based term developed for *Math Expressions*

shortest

The paper clip is the **shortest**.

Show All Totals Method*

$$
\begin{array}{r}
25 \\
+\ 48 \\
\hline
60 \\
13 \\
\hline
73
\end{array}
$$

shrinking pattern

4 3 2 1

side

← side

sort

You can **sort** the animals into groups.

sphere

square

square corner

square corner

sticks and circles*

1	○
11	|○
21	||○
31	|||○

*A classroom research-based term developed for *Math Expressions*

Glossary

subtract

$8 - 3 = 5$

subtraction story problem

8 flies are on a log.
6 are eaten by a frog.
How many flies are left?

switch the partners*

 $7 + 2$

 $2 + 7$

T

tally mark

Vegetables	Tally Marks	Number
Carrots	IIII	5
Corn	IIII	4
Peppers	IIII II	7

teen number

11 12 13 14 15 16 17 18 19

teen numbers

teen total*

14 ← teen total

9   5

tens

tens

56 has 5 **tens**.

total

$4 + 3 = 7$ $\begin{array}{r} 4 \\ + 3 \\ \hline 7 \end{array}$

total

trapezoid

*A classroom research-based term developed for *Math Expressions*

triangle

U

unknown partner*

$$4 + \boxed{} = 7$$

unknown total*

$$5 + 3 = \boxed{}$$

V

vertex

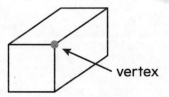

vertex

vertical form

$$\begin{array}{r} 6 \\ + 3 \\ \hline 9 \end{array} \qquad \begin{array}{r} 9 \\ - 3 \\ \hline 6 \end{array}$$

Z

zero

There are **zero** apples on the plate.

*A classroom research-based term developed for *Math Expressions*

1.ARO Algebraic Reasoning and Operations

1.ARO.1	Solve addition and subtraction word problems that involve adding to, putting together, taking from, taking apart, and comparing and have unknown quantities in all positions; represent problems using words, objects, drawings, length-based models (connecting cubes), numerals, number lines, as well as equations with a symbol for the unknown quantity.	Unit 1 Lessons 2, 3, 4, 5, 6, 7, 8; Unit 2 Lessons 1, 2, 3, 4, 6, 8, 10, 11, 12, 13, 14, 15, 16; Unit 3 Lessons 2, 3, 4, 5, 6, 7, 8, 9, 10, 11, 12; Unit 4 Lesson 5; Unit 5 Lessons 1, 2, 3, 4, 5, 11; Unit 6 Lessons 1, 2, 3, 4, 5, 6, 7, 8, 9
1.ARO.2	Solve addition word problems that involve three addends with a sum less than or equal to 20; represent a problem using objects or pictures or other methods, and equations that have a symbol for the unknown quantity.	Unit 5 Lessons 6, 11; Unit 6 Lessons 1, 4, 5, 9
1.ARO.3	Add and subtract applying the properties of operations.	Unit 1 Lessons 3, 4, 5, 6, 7, 8, 9; Unit 2 Lessons 7, 8, 9, 13; Unit 3 Lesson 5; Unit 4 Lessons 5, 10; Unit 5 Lessons 4, 6
1.ARO.4	Understand that a subtraction problem can be thought of as an unknown addend situation.	Unit 3 Lessons 6, 7, 8, 9, 10, 12; Unit 5 Lessons 2, 5, 10
1.ARO.5	Recognize the relationship between addition/subtraction and counting and understand that counting strategies can be used to add and subtract.	Unit 1 Lessons 1, 2, 3, 4, 9; Unit 2 Lessons 5, 6, 7, 8, 9; Unit 3 Lessons 1, 3, 4, 6, 7, 11; Unit 4 Lessons 1, 4, 5, 7, 15, 16, 17; Unit 5 Lessons 1, 2, 4

1.ARO.6	Fluently add and subtract through 10. Know how to add and subtract through 20 using strategies such as: for addition, *count on; make a ten* (example: $7 + 5 = 7 + 3 + 2$, so $7 + 3 + 2 = 10 + 2$, and $10 + 2 = 12$); *make an easier equal sum* (example: $9 + 6 = ?$, think $9 + 1 + 5 = 10 + 5$, so $10 + 5 = 15$; for subtraction, *decompose a number to get ten* (example: $17 - 8 = 17 - 7 - 1$, think $17 - 7 = 10$ and $10 - 1 = 9$); *use a related addition to subtract* (example: if you know $5 + 6 = 11$, then you can find $11 - 5 = 6$).	Unit 1 Lessons 3, 4, 5, 6, 7, 8, 9; Unit 2 Lessons 1, 2, 3, 5, 6, 7, 8, 9, 10, 11, 12, 13, 14, 15, 16; Unit 3 Lessons 1, 3, 4, 5, 6, 7, 10, 12; Unit 4 Lessons 4, 5, 6, 10, 15; Unit 5 Lessons 1, 2, 3, 4, 5, 10, 11; Unit 6 Lessons 3, 8; Unit 7 Lessons 5, 8, 13; Unit 8 Lesson 5
1.ARO.7	Know the meaning of the equal sign; decide whether or not an equation that involves addition or subtraction is true or false.	Unit 2 Lessons 3, 4, 11, 12, 13, 16; Unit 3 Lesson 12; Unit 5 Lesson 11
1.ARO.8	Find the unknown number in an addition or subtraction equation (examples: $9 + ? = 12$; $8 = ? - 5$; $7 + 2 = ?$).	Unit 1 Lessons 3, 4, 5, 6, 7, 8; Unit 2 Lessons 5, 6, 7, 8, 9, 10, 12, 13, 14, 16; Unit 3 Lessons 3, 4, 5, 6, 7, 8, 9, 11, 12; Unit 4 Lessons 4, 5, 6, 10, 13, 14, 15, 16; Unit 5 Lessons 1, 2, 3, 4, 5, 10; Unit 6 Lessons 6, 7
1.ARO.9	Create simple patterns using objects, pictures, numbers and rules. Identify possible rules to complete or extend patterns. Patterns may be repeating, growing or shrinking. Calculators can be used to create and explore patterns.	Unit 1 Lessons 10, 11; Unit 5 Lesson 9

1.PVO Place Value and Operations

1.PVO.1	Count, with or without objects, forward and backward to 120, starting at any number less than 120. For the number sequence to 120, read and write the corresponding numerals; represent a group of objects with a written numeral, addition and subtraction, pictures, tally marks, number lines and manipulatives, such as bundles of sticks and base 10 blocks. Skip count by 2s, 5s, and 10s.	Unit 4 Lessons 1, 2, 7, 8, 9, 10, 11, 15, 16, 18; Unit 5 Lessons 7, 8, 9; Unit 6 Lessons 4, 5

1.PVO.2	For a two-digit number, understand that the digit to the right represents ones and the digit to the left represents tens.	Unit 4 Lessons 1, 2, 3, 4, 7, 8, 9, 10, 11, 12, 13, 14, 16, 17, 18; Unit 5 Lessons 7, 8, 9; Unit 8 Lesson 1
1.PVO.2.a	Understand that 10 can be thought of as a group of ten ones named *ten*.	Unit 4 Lessons 1, 2, 3, 4, 9, 10, 16, 18; Unit 5 Lessons 8, 10; Unit 8 Lesson 1
1.PVO.2.b	Understand that the numbers 11 through 19 are made up of one ten and one through nine ones.	Unit 4 Lessons 2, 3, 4, 5, 8, 10; Unit 5 Lesson 8
1.PVO.2.c	Know that the decade numbers 10 through 90 represent one through nine tens and zero ones.	Unit 4 Lessons 1, 7, 8, 9, 13, 14, 18; Unit 5 Lesson 10; Unit 8 Lesson 1
1.PVO.3	Apply place value concepts to compare two 2-digit numbers using the symbols >, <, and =.	Unit 4 Lessons 3, 12, 16, 18; Unit 8 Lesson 6
1.PVO.4	Add numbers through 100, such as a two-digit number and a one-digit number or a two-digit number and a multiple of ten. Understand that groups of objects or drawings and strategies can be used to find sums (examples of strategies: *relationship between addition and subtraction, place value, properties of operations*) and explain how the strategy and recorded result are related. Know that to add two-digit numbers, ones are added to ones and tens are added to tens and in some instances, ten ones will result in making one ten.	Unit 4 Lessons 9, 10, 11, 13, 14, 15, 16, 17, 18; Unit 5 Lessons 9, 10, 11; Unit 8 Lessons 1, 2, 3, 4, 5, 6
1.PVO.5	Use mental math to find a number that is 10 more or 10 less than any given two-digit number (without using counting) and explain the reasoning used to find the result.	Unit 5 Lessons 8, 9
1.PVO.6	For numbers 10 through 90, subtract multiples of 10 resulting in differences of 0 through 80. Use groups of objects or pictures and strategies to subtract. Strategies can include place value concepts, the relationship between addition and subtraction, and properties of operations. Explain how the strategy and recorded result are related.	Unit 5 Lessons 9, 10, 11; Unit 8 Lesson 6

1.MDA Measurement and Data Analysis

1.MDA.1	Compare to order three items by length. Compare the lengths of two items using a third item (indirect comparison).	Unit 7 Lessons 12, 14
1.MDA.2	Determine the length of an object by placing as many same-size smaller units end-to-end as needed along the span of the object ensuring no gaps or overlaps. Understand that length of the object is the number of same-size units that were used. (Note: The number of "length-units" should not extend beyond the end of the object being measured.)	Unit 7 Lessons 13, 14
1.MDA.3	Use analog and digital clocks to express time orally and in written form in hours and half-hours.	Unit 7 Lessons 1, 2, 3, 4, 5, 14
1.MDA.4	Organize, represent, and interpret data with up to three categories using picture graphs, bar graphs, and tally charts. Ask questions and provide answers about how many in all comprise the data and how many are in each category. Compare the number in one category to that in another category.	Unit 6 Lessons 1, 2, 3, 4, 5, 9
1.MDA.5	Recognize and identify coins (penny, nickel, dime, and quarter) and their value and use the ¢ (cent) symbol appropriately.	Unit 2 Lesson 7; Unit 4, Lessons 8, 19, 20
1.MDA.6	Know the comparative values of all U.S. coins (e.g. a dime is of greater value than a nickel). Find equivalent values (e.g., a nickel is equivalent to 5 pennies.) Solve problems and use the values of the coins in the solutions of the problems.	Unit 2 Lesson 7; Unit 4 Lessons 8, 19, 20
1.MDA.7	Explore dimes and pennies as they relate to place value concepts.	Unit 4 Lessons 8, 19, 20

1.GSR Geometry and Spatial Reasoning

1.GSR.1	Understand the difference between defining attributes of a figure (examples: a square has 4 sides of equal length and 4 vertices) and non-defining attributes (examples: size, color, position). Using concrete materials and paper and pencil, build and draw geometric figures according to their defining attributes.	Unit 7 Lessons 6, 7, 8, 9, 10
1.GSR.2	Create composite geometric figures by putting together two-dimensional figures (triangles, squares, rectangles, trapezoids, half-circles, and quarter-circles) or three-dimensional figures (cubes, rectangular prisms, cylinders, and cones), then form a new figure from the composite figure.	Unit 7 Lessons 9, 10, 11
1.GSR.3	Separate rectangles and circles into two or four equal shares, and use the words *halves, fourths,* and *quarters*, and the phrases *half of, fourth of,* and *quarter of* to identify the equal-size shares. Use the terms "two of" or " four of" to describe the number of equal shares in the whole. Understand that when a figure is separated into more equal shares, the size of the shares is smaller.	Unit 7 Lessons 8, 9, 14

Mathematical Processes and Practices

MPP1

Problem Solving

Unit 1 Lessons 2, 3, 4, 6, 8, 9, 10, 11
Unit 2 Lessons 1, 2, 3, 4, 6, 7, 8, 9, 10, 13, 14, 16
Unit 3 Lessons 1, 2, 3, 4, 6, 7, 8, 9, 10, 11, 12
Unit 4 Lessons 2, 3, 5, 10, 18, 19, 20
Unit 5 Lessons 1, 2, 3, 4, 5, 6, 9, 11
Unit 6 Lessons 1, 2, 4, 5, 6, 7, 8, 9
Unit 7 Lessons 8, 12, 14
Unit 8 Lessons 1, 3, 4, 6

MPP2

Abstract and Quantitative Reasoning

Unit 1 Lessons 3, 4, 5, 6, 7, 8, 9
Unit 2 Lessons 1, 2, 3, 4, 6, 10, 11, 12, 13, 15, 16
Unit 3 Lessons 3, 5, 6, 12
Unit 4 Lessons 1, 3, 4, 6, 7, 8, 9, 10, 11, 12, 14, 15, 16, 17, 18, 19
Unit 5 Lessons 1, 2, 3, 4, 5, 9, 10, 11
Unit 6 Lessons 1, 2, 3, 5, 6, 8, 9
Unit 7 Lessons 8, 9, 14
Unit 8 Lessons 1, 2, 3, 4, 5, 6

MPP3

Use and Evaluate Logical Reasoning

Unit 1 Lessons 1, 2, 3, 4, 5, 6, 7, 8, 9, 10
Unit 2 Lessons 1, 2, 3, 4, 6, 7, 8, 9, 10, 11, 12, 13, 14, 16
Unit 3 Lessons 2, 3, 4, 6, 7, 8, 9, 10, 11, 12
Unit 4 Lessons 1, 2, 3, 4, 5, 6, 7, 8, 9, 10, 11, 12, 13, 14, 15, 16, 17, 18, 19, 20
Unit 5 Lessons 1, 2, 3, 4, 5, 6, 7, 8, 9, 10, 11
Unit 6 Lessons 1, 2, 3, 4, 5, 6, 7, 8, 9
Unit 7 Lessons 1, 2, 3, 4, 5, 6, 7, 8, 9, 10, 11, 12, 13, 14
Unit 8 Lessons 1, 2, 3, 4, 5, 6

MPP4

Mathematical Modeling

Unit 1 Lessons 2, 3, 9
Unit 2 Lessons 1, 2, 6, 10, 13, 16
Unit 3 Lessons 1, 2, 5, 6, 7, 8, 9, 10, 11, 12
Unit 4 Lessons 2, 3, 4, 5, 10, 18, 19, 20
Unit 5 Lessons 1, 2, 3, 4, 6, 8, 9, 11
Unit 6 Lessons 2, 3, 4, 5, 6, 7, 8, 9
Unit 7 Lessons 3, 8, 12, 14
Unit 8 Lessons 1, 2, 3, 6

MPP5

Use Mathematical Tools

Unit 1 Lessons 1, 2, 3, 4, 5, 6, 7, 8, 9
Unit 2 Lessons 5, 6, 7, 8, 16
Unit 3 Lessons 1, 2, 3, 4, 7, 11
Unit 4 Lessons 1, 2, 3, 4, 5, 6, 7, 8, 9, 10, 11, 12, 13, 14, 16, 17, 18, 19
Unit 5 Lessons 1, 2, 6, 7, 8, 9, 10, 11
Unit 6 Lessons 3, 4, 5, 8, 9
Unit 7 Lessons 1, 2, 5, 6, 7, 8, 9, 10, 11, 12, 13, 14
Unit 8 Lessons 2, 3, 6

MPP6

Use Precise Mathematical Language

Unit 1 Lessons 1, 2, 3, 4, 5, 6, 7, 8, 9, 10
Unit 2 Lessons 1, 3, 4, 5, 6, 7, 8, 9, 10, 11, 12, 13, 14, 16
Unit 3 Lessons 1, 2, 3, 4, 5, 6, 7, 8, 9, 10, 11, 12
Unit 4 Lessons 1, 2, 3, 4, 5, 6, 7, 8, 9, 10, 11, 12, 13, 14, 15, 16, 17, 18, 19, 20
Unit 5 Lessons 1, 2, 3, 4, 5, 6, 7, 8, 9, 10, 11
Unit 6 Lessons 1, 2, 3, 4, 5, 6, 7, 8, 9
Unit 7 Lessons 1, 2, 3, 4, 5, 6, 7, 8, 9, 10, 11, 12, 13, 14
Unit 8 Lessons 1, 2, 3, 4, 5, 6

MPP7

See Structure

Unit 1 Lessons 1, 2, 3, 4, 5, 6, 7, 8, 9, 10, 11
Unit 2 Lessons 13, 14, 16
Unit 3 Lessons 1, 3, 9, 12
Unit 4 Lessons 1, 2, 3, 5, 6, 7, 8, 9, 10,13, 17, 18, 19
Unit 5 Lessons 1, 2, 3, 5, 6, 7, 8, 9, 10, 11
Unit 6 Lessons 6, 8, 9
Unit 7 Lessons 1, 2, 3, 4, 5, 6, 7, 9, 10, 11, 14
Unit 8 Lessons 2, 6

MPP8

Generalize

Unit 1 Lessons 1, 2, 3, 4, 5, 6, 7, 8, 9
Unit 2 Lessons 6, 7, 8, 11, 14, 16
Unit 3 Lessons 8, 9, 12
Unit 4 Lessons 1, 2, 5, 6, 7, 9, 10, 12, 13, 14, 15, 17, 18
Unit 5 Lessons 1, 2, 4, 5, 6, 7, 8, 9, 10, 11
Unit 6 Lessons 1, 6, 7, 9
Unit 7 Lessons 3, 6, 7, 8, 9, 10, 12, 14
Unit 8 Lessons 1, 2, 4, 6

Index

B

C

D

Index

Index

Illustrator: Josh Brill

Did you ever try to use shapes to draw animals like the frog on the cover?

Over the last 10 years Josh has been using geometric shapes to design his animals. His aim is to keep the animal drawings simple and use color to make them appealing.

Add some color to the frog Josh drew. Then try drawing a cat or dog or some other animal using the shapes below.

Shape Toolbox